Tensile Testing

Edited by

Patricia Han

**The Materials
Information Society**

Materials Park, OH 44073-0002

Library of Congress Catalog Card Number: 92-71900
ISBN: 0-87170-440-4
SAN: 204-7586

Production Coordinator
Randall Boring

Production Assistant
Thomas Moore

Printed in the United States of America

Preface

Mechanical testing of materials is generally performed for one of the following reasons:

- *Test development:* to create or refine the test method itself
- *Design:* to create or select materials for specific applications
- *Quality control:* to verify that incoming material is acceptable

Uniaxial tensile testing is one of the most frequently performed mechanical tests. This type of test generally involves gripping a specimen at both ends and subjecting it to increasing axial load until it breaks. Recording of load and elongation data during the test allows the investigator to determine several characteristics about the mechanical behavior of the material. These tensile properties are one of the first topics covered in many undergraduate courses on mechanics of engineering materials. Numerous materials references, whether they are engineering handbooks or materials specifications, include such tensile data.

If tensile testing is so popular, and its data so widely used, then why devote a new book to the subject? One reason is the proliferation of new engineering materials, developed in response to changing performance requirements. Consequently, increasing numbers of people need either to perform tensile tests or to use the resultant information. To obtain meaningful data, one needs to understand the factors that affect test results; to use tensile data effectively, one needs to understand the links between actual material behavior and the numbers generated by tests.

Our vision for this book was to provide a volume that could serve not only as an introduction for those who are just starting to perform tensile tests and use tensile data, but also as a source of more detailed information for those who are better acquainted with the subject. We have written this reference book to appeal to laboratory managers, technicians, students, designers, and materials engineers.

The first part of this book opens with an overview that introduces the newcomer to the fundamentals and language of tensile testing. The succeeding chapters discuss methodology and equipment in an effort to provide understanding of good general testing practice.

The second part consists of separate chapters on tensile testing of frequently studied classes of engineering materials. These chapters highlight factors that are of particular importance in the testing of these materials; they also discuss how to use the resultant data effectively.

This book would not have been possible without the voluntary efforts of the contributing authors. We are also grateful for the valuable comments and suggestions provided by the following reviewers: F.J. Marsh, Bethlehem Steel Corp.; D.K. Matlock, Colorado School of Mines; J.C. Vicic, FMC Corp.; G.A. Gadoua and G. Lewis, General Motors Corp.; D.W. Demianczuk, LTV Steel Corp.; K.K. Biegler, D.G. Chasco, C.G. Larsen, and L.G. Mosiman, MTS Systems Corp.; D.J. Meuleman, National Steel Corp.; W.A. Kawahara, Sandia National Laboratories—Livermore; and A. Graf, University of Michigan. Thanks are also due to the Tinius Olsen Company, Instron Corp. and MB Systems Corp. for providing illustrations.

Patricia Han
MTS Systems Corporation

Contents

1

Overview of Tensile Testing

William F. Hosford, University of Michigan

There are several reasons for performing tensile tests. The results of tensile tests are used in selecting materials for engineering applications. Tensile properties frequently are included in material specifications to ensure quality. Tensile properties often are measured during development of new materials and processes, so that different materials and processes can be compared. Finally, tensile properties often are used to predict the behavior of a material under forms of loading other than uniaxial tension.

The strength of a material often is the primary concern. The strength of interest may be measured in terms of either the stress necessary to cause appreciable plastic deformation or the maximum stress that the material can withstand. These measures of strength are used, with appropriate caution (in the form of safety factors), in engineering design. Also of interest is the material's ductility, which is a measure of how much it can be deformed before it fractures. Rarely is ductility incorporated directly in design; rather, it is included in material specifications to ensure quality and toughness. Low ductility in a tensile test often is accompanied by low resistance to fracture under other forms of loading. Elastic properties also may be of interest, but special techniques must be used to measure these properties during tensile testing, and more accurate measurements can be made by ultrasonic techniques.

Tensile Specimens

Consider the typical tensile specimen shown in Fig. 1. It has enlarged ends or shoulders for gripping. The important part of the specimen is the gage section. The cross-sectional area of the gage section is reduced relative to that of the remainder of the specimen so that deformation and failure will be localized in this region. The gage length

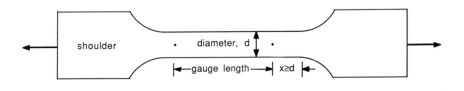

Fig 1. Typical tensile specimen, showing a reduced gage section and enlarged shoulders. To avoid end effects from the shoulders, the length of the transition region should be at least as great as the diameter, and the total length of the reduced section should be at least four times the diameter.

is the region over which measurements are made and is centered within the reduced section. The distances between the ends of the gage section and the shoulders should be great enough so that the larger ends do not constrain deformation within the gage section, and the gage length should be great relative to its diameter. Otherwise, the stress state will be more complex than simple tension. Detailed descriptions of standard specimen shapes are given in subsequent chapters on tensile testing of specific materials.

There are various ways of gripping the specimen, some of which are illustrated in Fig. 2. The end may be screwed into a threaded grip, or it may be pinned; butt ends may be used, or the grip section may be held between wedges. There are still other methods. The most important

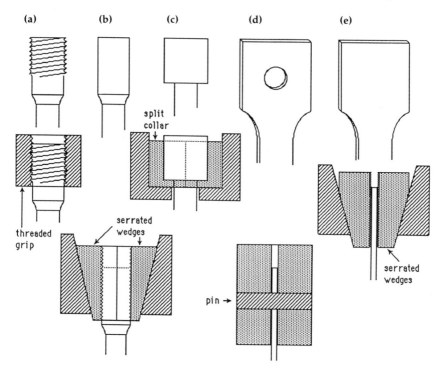

Fig 2. Systems for gripping tensile specimens. For round specimens, these include threaded grips (a), serrated wedges (b), and, for butt end specimens, split collars constrained by a solid collar (c). Sheet specimens may be gripped with pins (d) or serrated wedges (e).

concern in the selection of a gripping method is to ensure that the specimen can be held at the maximum load without slippage or failure in the grip section. Bending should be minimized.

Stress-Strain Curves

A tensile test involves mounting the specimen in a machine and subjecting it to tension. The tensile force is recorded as a function of the increase in gage length. Figure 3(a) shows a typical curve for a ductile material. Such plots of tensile force versus tensile elongation would be of little value if they were not normalized with respect to specimen dimensions.

Engineering stress, or nominal stress, S, is defined as

$$S = F/A_0 \qquad\qquad \text{(Eq 1)}$$

where F is the tensile force and A_0 is the initial cross-sectional area of the gage section.

Engineering strain, or nominal strain, e, is defined as

$$e = \Delta L/L_0 \qquad\qquad \text{(Eq 2)}$$

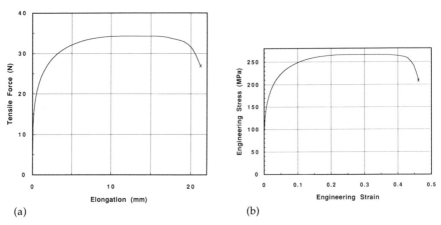

(a)   (b)

Fig 3. (a) Load-elongation curve from a tensile test and (b) corresponding engineering stress-strain curve. Specimen diameter, 12.5 mm; gage length, 50 mm.

where L_0 is the initial gage length and ΔL is the change in gage length ($L - L_0$).

When force-elongation data are converted to engineering stress and strain, a stress-strain curve (Fig 3b) that is identical in shape to the force-elongation curve can be plotted. The advantage of dealing with stress versus strain rather than load versus elongation is that the stress-strain curve is virtually independent of specimen dimensions.

Elastic Versus Plastic Deformation

When a solid material is subjected to small stresses, the bonds between the atoms are stretched. When the stress is removed, the bonds relax and the material returns to its original shape. This reversible deformation is called *elastic deformation*. (The deformation of a rubber band is entirely elastic.) At higher stresses, planes of atoms slide over one another. This deformation, which is not recovered when the stress is removed, is termed *plastic deformation*. Note that the term "plastic deformation" does not mean that the deformed material is a plastic (a polymeric material). Bending of a wire (such as paper-clip wire) with the fingers (Fig 4) illustrates the difference. If the wire is bent a little bit, it will snap back when released (top). With larger bends, it will unbend elastically to some extent on release, but there will be a permanent bend because of the plastic deformation (bottom).

For most materials, the initial portion of the curve is linear. The slope of this linear region is called the *elastic modulus* or *Young's modulus*:

$$E = S/e \tag{Eq 3}$$

In the elastic range, the ratio, υ, of the magnitude of the lateral contraction strain to the axial strain is called *Poisson's ratio*:

$$\upsilon = -e_y/e_x \text{ (in an x-direction tensile test)} \tag{Eq 4}$$

Because elastic strains are usually very small, reasonably accurate measurement of Young's modulus and Poisson's ratio in a tensile test requires that strain be measured with a very sensitive extensometer. (Strain gages should be used for lateral strains.) Accurate results can also be obtained by velocity-of-sound measurements (unless the modulus is very low or the damping is high, as with polymers).

5

Tensile Testing

When the stress rises high enough, the stress-strain behavior will cease to be linear and the strain will not disappear completely on unloading. The strain that remains is called plastic strain. The first plastic strain usually corresponds to the first deviation from linearity. (For some materials, the elastic deformation may be nonlinear, and so there is not always this correspondence.) Once plastic deformation has begun, there will be both elastic and plastic contributions to the total

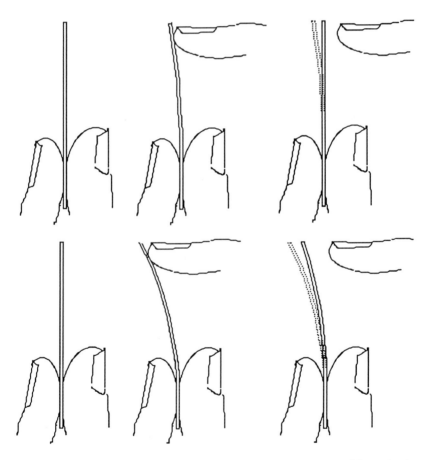

Fig 4. Elastic and plastic deformation of a wire with the fingers. With small forces (top), all of the bending is elastic and disappears when the force is released. With greater forces (below), some of the bending is recoverable (elastic), but most of the bending is not recovered (is plastic) when the force is removed.

strain, e_T. This can be expressed as $e_T = e_e + e_p$, where e_p is the plastic contribution and e_e is the elastic contribution (and still related to the stress by Eq 3).

It is tempting to define an *elastic limit* as the stress at which plastic deformation first occurs and a *proportional limit* as the stress at which the stress-strain curve first deviates from linearity. However, neither definition is very useful, because measurement of the stress at which plastic deformation first occurs or the first deviation from linearity is observed depends on how accurately strain can be measured. The smaller the plastic strains that can be sensed and the smaller the deviations from linearity can be detected, the smaller the elastic and proportional limits.

To avoid this problem, the onset of the plasticity is usually described by an offset *yield strength*, which can be measured with greater reproducibility. It can be found by constructing a straight line parallel to the

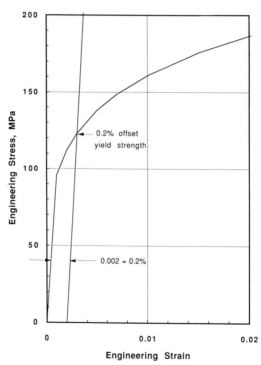

Fig 5. The low-strain region of the stress-strain curve for a ductile material

initial linear portion of the stress-strain curve, but offset by $e = 0.002$ or 0.2%. The yield strength is the stress at which this line intersects the stress-strain curve (Fig 5). The rationale is that if the material had been loaded to this stress and then unloaded, the unloading path would have been along this offset line and would have resulted in a plastic strain of $e = 0.2\%$. Other offset strains are sometimes used. The advantage of defining yield strength in this way is that such a parameter is easily reproduced and does not depend heavily on the sensitivity of measurement.

Sometimes, for convenience, yielding in metals is defined by the stress required to achieve a specified total strain (e.g., $e_T = 0.005$ or 0.5% elongation) instead of a specified offset strain. In any case, the criterion should be made clear to the user of the data.

Yield Points

For some materials (e.g., low-carbon steels and many linear polymers), the stress-strain curves have initial maxima followed by lower stresses, as shown in Fig. 6(a) and (b). After the initial maximum, all the deformation at any instant is occurring within a relatively small region of the specimen. Continued elongation of the specimen occurs by propagation of the deforming region (Lüders band in the case of steels) along the gage section rather than by increased strain within the

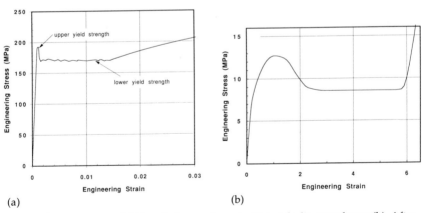

(a)   (b)

Fig 6. Inhomogeneous yielding of a low-carbon steel (a) and a linear polymer (b). After the initial stress maxima, the deformation occurs within a narrow band, which propagates along the entire length of the gage section before the stress rises again.

deforming region. Only after the entire gage section has been traversed by the band does the stress rise again. In the case of linear polymers, a yield strength is often defined as the initial maximum stress. For steels, the subsequent *lower* yield strength is used to describe yielding. This is because measurements of the initial maximum or *upper* yield strength are extremely sensitive to how axially the load is applied during the tensile test. Some laboratories cite the minimum, whereas others cite a mean stress during this discontinuous yielding.

The tensile strength (ultimate strength) is defined as the highest value of engineering stress* (Fig 7). Up to the maximum load, the deformation should be uniform along the gage section. With ductile materials, the tensile strength corresponds to the point at which the deformation starts to localize, forming a neck (Fig 7a). Less ductile materials fracture before they neck (Fig 7b). In this case, the fracture strength is the tensile strength. Indeed, very brittle materials (e.g., glass at room temperature) do not yield before fracture (Fig. 7c). Such materials have tensile strengths but not yield strengths.

Ductility

There are two common measures used to describe the ductility of a material. One is the percent elongation, which is defined simply as

$$\%El = [(L_f - L_0)/L_0] \times 100 \qquad \text{(Eq 5)}$$

where L_0 is the initial gage length and L_f is the length of the gage section at fracture. Measurements may be made on the broken pieces or under load. For most materials, the amount of elastic elongation is so small that the two are equivalent. When this is not so (as with brittle metals or rubber), the results should state whether or not the elongation includes an elastic contribution. The other common measure of ductility is percent reduction in area, which is defined as

$$\%RA = [(A_0 - A_f)/A_0] \times 100 \qquad \text{(Eq 6)}$$

---

* Sometimes the upper yield strength of low-carbon steel is higher than the subsequent maximum. In such cases, some people prefer to define the tensile strength as the subsequent maximum instead of the initial maximum, which is higher. In such cases, the definition of tensile strength should be made clear to the user.

where A_0 and A_f are the initial cross-sectional area and the cross sectional area at fracture, respectively. If failure occurs without necking, one can be calculated from the other:

$$\%El = \%RA / (100 - \%RA) \qquad \text{(Eq 7)}$$

After a neck has developed, the two are no longer related. Percent elongation, as a measure of ductility, has the disadvantage that it is really composed of two parts: the uniform elongation that occurs before necking, and the localized elongation that occurs during necking. The second part is sensitive to the specimen shape. When a gage section that is very long (relative to its diameter), the necking elongation converted to percent is very small. In contrast, with a gage section that is short (relative to its diameter), the necking elongation can account for most of the total elongation.

For round bars, this problem has been remedied by standardizing the ratio of gage length to diameter to 4:1. Within a series of bars, all with the same gage-length-to-diameter ratio, the necking elongation will be the same fraction of the total elongation. However, there is no simple way to make meaningful comparisons of percent elongation from such standardized bars with that measured on sheet tensile specimens or wire. With sheet tensile specimens, a portion of the elongation occurs during diffuse necking, and this could be standardized by maintaining the same ratio of width to gage length. However, a portion of the

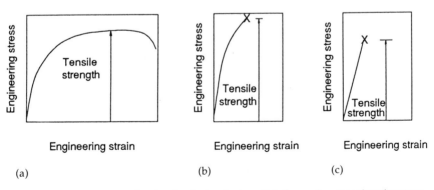

Fig 7. Stress-strain curves showing that the tensile strength is the maximum engineering stress regardless of whether the specimen necks (a) or fractures before necking (b and c).

elongation also occurs during what is called localized necking, and this depends on the sheet thickness. For tensile testing of wire, it is impractical to have a reduced section, and so the ratio of gage length to diameter is necessarily very large. Necking elongation contributes very little to the total elongation.

Percent reduction in area, as a measure of ductility, has the disadvantage that with very ductile materials it is often difficult to measure the final cross-sectional area at fracture. This is particularly true of sheet specimens.

True Stress and Strain

If the results of tensile testing are to be used to predict how a metal will behave under other forms of loading, it is desirable to plot the data in terms of true stress and true strain. True stress, σ, is defined as

$$\sigma = F/A \tag{Eq 8}$$

where A is the cross-sectional area at the time that the force is F. Up to the point at which necking starts, true strain, ε, is defined as

$$\varepsilon = \ln(L/L_0) \tag{Eq 9}$$

This definition arises from taking an increment of true strain, $d\varepsilon$, as the incremental change in length, dL, divided by the length, L, at the time, $d\varepsilon = dL/L$, and integrating. As long as the deformation is uniform along the gage section, the true stress and strain can be calculated from the engineering quantities. With constant volume and uniform deformation, $LA = L_0A_0$:

$$A_0/A = L/L_0 \tag{Eq 10}$$

Thus, according to Eq 2, $A_0/A = 1 + e$. Equation 8 can be rewritten as

$$\sigma = (F/A_0)(A_0/A)$$

and, with substitution for A_0/A and F/A_0, as

$$\sigma = S\,(1 + e) \tag{Eq 11}$$

Substitution of $L/L_0 = 1 + e$ into the expression for true strain (Eq 9) gives

$$\varepsilon = \ln(1 + e) \qquad\qquad\qquad\qquad (\text{Eq } 12)$$

At very low strains, the differences between true and engineering stress and strain are very small. It does not really matter whether Young's modulus is defined in terms of engineering or true stress strain.

It must be emphasized that these expressions are valid only as long as the deformation is uniform. Once necking starts, Eq 8 for true stress is still valid, but the cross-sectional area at the base of the neck must be measured directly rather than being inferred from the length measurements. Because the true stress, thus calculated, is the true stress at the base of the neck, the corresponding true strain should also be at the base of the neck. Equation 9 could still be used if the L and L_0 values were known for an extremely short gage section centered on the middle of the neck (one so short that variations of area along it would be negligible). Of course, there will be no such gage section, but if there were, Eq 10 would be valid. Thus the true strain can be calculated as

$$\varepsilon = \ln(A_0/A) \qquad\qquad\qquad\qquad (\text{Eq } 13)$$

Figure 8 shows a comparison of engineering and true stress-strain curves for the same material.

Bridgman Correction

When the neck becomes sharp, the stress state at the center of the neck is no longer uniaxial tension. As the material in the center is being stretched in the axial direction, it must contract in the lateral directions. This contraction is resisted by the adjacent regions, which have larger cross sections and therefore are no longer deforming. The net effect is triaxial tension in the central region with lateral stresses as well as the axial tension. The stress distribution across the neck is shown in Fig. 9.

According to yielding theories, only that part of the axial stress that exceeds the lateral stress contributes to plastic flow. Bridgman devised a simple way to determine this corrected true stress, σ, from the measured true stress, σ (= F/A), the radius of the specimen at the base of the neck, a (= $D/2$), and the radius of curvature of the neck profile, R:

$$\overline{\sigma}/\sigma_{z(av)} = \{(1 + 2R/a) \ln [1 + a/(2R)]\}^{-1} \qquad \text{(Eq 14)}$$

Figure 10 is a plot of $\overline{\sigma}/\sigma_{z(av)}$ versus a/R. A simple way of measuring the radius of curvature, R, of the neck is to slide a calibrated cone along the neck until it just becomes tangent at the base of the neck.

The problem is even more complex. Once the neck becomes severe enough for the correction to be important, the state of hydrostatic tension at the center is likely to cause internal fracture by growth and linking of voids, so that the tensile load is no longer carriedby the full cross section. Therefore, true stresses calculated from tensile data taken after severe necking has occurred are of little use.

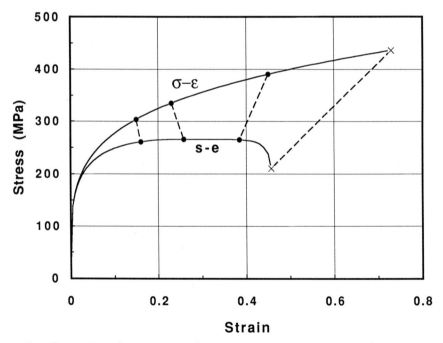

Fig 8. Comparison of engineering and true stress-strain curves. Prior to necking, a point on the σ-ε curve can be constructed from a point on the s-e curve using Eq 11 and 12. Subsequently, the cross section must be measured to find true stress and strain.

13

Mathematical Approximations of the True Stress-Strain Curve

True stress-strain curves for ductile metals often can be approximated mathematically by power-law hardening:

$$\sigma = K\varepsilon^n \qquad\qquad\qquad \text{(Eq 15)}$$

where n is the *strain-hardening exponent* and K is the *strength coefficient*. With this expression, the true stress-strain relationship plots as a straight line on a log-log plot, as shown in Fig. 11. The exponent, n, is the slope of the plot. K can be found by extrapolating the curve to $\varepsilon = 1$ and taking the value of σ at this point, because if $\varepsilon = 1$ in Eq 15, $\sigma = K$. The level of n is particularly significant in sheet-metal forming operations because it is a good indication of the ability of the sheet to distribute the strain over a

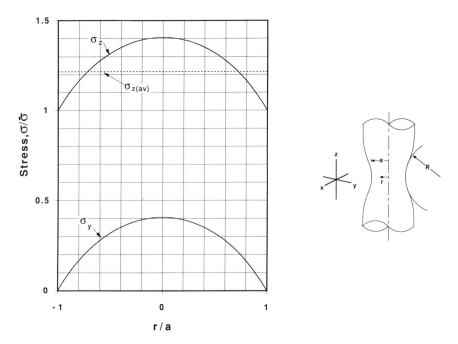

Fig 9. Stress distribution across the neck when $a/R = 1$ (left), and the corresponding geometry of the neck (right). Both the axial and lateral stresses are the most tensile at the center of the neck. The values of the stresses are normalized by the effective stress, $\bar{\sigma}$.

wide region. Often the log-log plot of the true stress-strain relationship deviates from linearity at low strains and/or high strains. In such cases, it is still convenient to use Eq 15 for the strain range over which the log-log plot is linear. The value of n is taken as the slope of the linear region on the log-log plot:

$$n = d\,(\ln\sigma)/d\,(\ln\varepsilon) = (\varepsilon/\sigma)\,d\sigma/d\varepsilon \qquad\qquad\text{(Eq 16)}$$

Sometimes other mathematical approximations of the true stress-strain curve give better fits, particularly expressions with more empirical constants. Some of the expressions used are:

$$\sigma = K'\,(\varepsilon + \varepsilon_0)^{n'} \qquad\qquad\text{(Eq 17)}$$

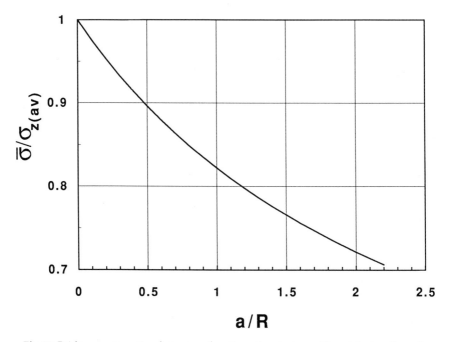

Fig 10. Bridgman correction factor as a function of neck shape. The plot gives the ratio of the effective stress to the axial stress for measured values of a/R.

$$\sigma = \sigma_0 + K''\varepsilon^{n''} \tag{Eq 18}$$

$$\sigma = \sigma_0 [1 - \exp(-b\varepsilon)] \tag{Eq 19}$$

It should be realized that the constants n' and K' in Eq 17 and n'' and K'' in Eq 18 are not the same as n and K in the more commonly used Eq 15.

Strain Rate

The effect of strain rate on the stress-strain curve is frequently neglected. For most metallic materials at room temperature, the strain rate has only a small effect on the level of the stress-strain curve. The average strain rate during most tests is in the range of 10^{-3} to 10^{-2}/s. (If, during the tensile test, a strain of $\varepsilon = 0.3$ is reached in 5 min, the average strain rate is $\dot{\varepsilon} = 10^{-3}$/s. A strain rate of $\dot{\varepsilon} = 10^{-2}$/s corresponds to reaching a strain of $\varepsilon = 0.3$ in 30 s.) For many materials, the

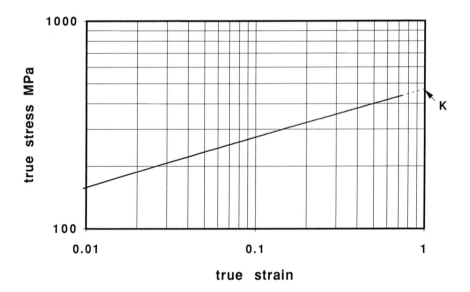

Fig 11. A plot of the true stress-strain curve on logarithmic scales. The straight line indicates that Eq 15 holds. The slope of the curve is n, and $K = \sigma$ at $\varepsilon = 1$.

effect of the strain rate on the stress, σ, at a fixed strain and temperature can be accounted for by the expression

$$\sigma = C\dot{\varepsilon}^m \qquad \text{(Eq 20)}$$

The exponent, m, is called the strain-rate sensitivity. Equation 20 predicts that the relative levels of σ at two strain rates is given by

$$\sigma_2/\sigma_1 = (\dot{\varepsilon}_2/\dot{\varepsilon}_1)^m \qquad \text{(Eq 21)}$$

At room temperature, the value of m is between -0.005 and $+0.015$ for most metals. For $m = 0.01$, a ten-fold increase in strain rate ($\dot{\varepsilon}_2/\dot{\varepsilon}_1 = 10$) raises the level of the stress by only 2%. Higher levels of m are found in polymeric materials and in metals at elevated temperatures. Even when the strain-rate sensitivity is low, it can have appreciable effects on how evenly the strain is distributed during sheet forming.

There are two ways of determining the value of m, as illustrated in Fig. 12. One is to compare the levels of stress, at the same strain, found in tensile tests run at two different strain rates. The other is to change the rate suddenly during a test and compare the levels of stress immediately before and immediately after the change. The latter method is easier and therefore more common. The two methods may give somewhat different values for m. In both cases, m is found from

$$m = \ln\,(\sigma_2/\sigma_1)/\ln\,(\dot{\varepsilon}_2/\dot{\varepsilon}_1) \qquad \text{(Eq 22)}$$

Temperature Rise

A tensile specimen can undergo an appreciable temperature rise during testing. This is because most of the mechanical energy, expended by the test machine in elongating the specimen, is converted to heat. The temperature rise is proportional to the amount of energy expended and to the fraction of the heat that is retained in the specimen. If the testing is rapid enough so that little heat is lost to the surroundings, the temperature rise can be surprisingly high. Consider, for example, a low-carbon steel specimen after a 22% extension ($\varepsilon = 0.20$). Assuming that 95% of the energy is retained as heat ($\alpha = 0.95$) and using typical properties for low-carbon steel

[K = 500 MPa (72.5 ksi), n = 0.22, density ρ = 7.88 Mg/m^3, and heat capacity C = 447 J/kg · °C], the calculated* temperature rise is 79 °C (142 °F). A temperature rise of this magnitude may cause significant changes in the properties being measured. For materials of higher strength, the temperature rise can be even higher.

With slow testing, much of the heat can be dissipated to the surroundings, whereas with rapid testing most of it is retained. The net effect is that there can be an apparent strain-rate effect that is caused by temperature changes during testing.

Sheet Anisotropy

If the tensile tests are performed on specimens cut from sheet material at different orientations to the prior rolling direction (Fig 13), there

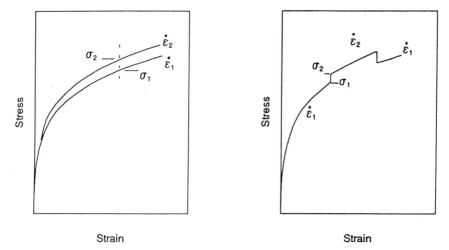

Fig 12. Two methods of determining the strain-rate sensitivity. Continuous stress-strain curves at different strain rates can be compared at the same strain (left), or sudden changes of strain rate can be made and the stress levels just before and just after the change compared (right). In both cases, Eq 21 can be used to find m. Typically ($\dot\varepsilon_2/\dot\varepsilon_1$) is about 10.

---

* Calculated from $\Delta T = (\alpha/\rho C) \int \sigma d\varepsilon = (\alpha/\rho C)K\varepsilon^{n+1}/(n+1)$ with consistent units.

may not be much difference between the stress-strain curves. However, the lack of variation of the stress-strain curves with direction does not indicate that the material is isotropic. The parameter that is commonly used to characterize the anisotropy of sheet metal is the *strain ratio* or *R-value* defined as the ratio, R^* of the contractile strains measured in a tensile test before necking occurs:

$$R = \varepsilon_w / \varepsilon_t \qquad \text{(Eq 23)}$$

where ε_w is the width strain, ln (w/w_0), and ε_t is the thickness strain, ln (t/t_0). The value of R would be equal to 1 for an isotropic material. Often, however, R is either greater or less than 1. For thin sheets, accurate direct measurement of the thickness strain is difficult. Therefore, the thickness

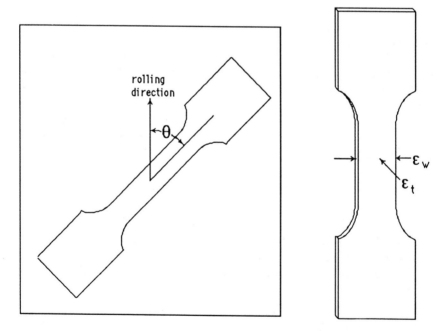

Fig 13. Tensile specimen cut from a rolled sheet (left). The *R*-value is the ratio of $\varepsilon_w/\varepsilon_t$ during extension (right).

---

* A lower-case *r* often is used instead of a capital *R* for the strain ratio; they are identical.

strain is often deduced from the constant-volume relationship, $\varepsilon_t = -\varepsilon_w - \varepsilon_l$, where ε_l is the length strain, $\ln (l/l_0)$. By substitution,

$$R = -\varepsilon_w/(\varepsilon_w + \varepsilon_l) \tag{Eq 24}$$

To avoid constraints from the grips, the strains should be measured on a gage section that is removed from the enlarged ends by a distance at least equal to the width of the specimen. Some workers suggest that the strains be measured when the elongation is about 15% as long as this is less than the strain at which necking starts.

Although the R-value usually does not change much during the tensile test, the strains at 15% are large enough to be measured with reasonable accuracy. The measurement of R is subject to greater error than may at first be apparent. If the accuracy of measuring strains were ± 0.01, the error in R would be $\pm 25\%$. Consider, for example, a material for which $R = 1$ ($\varepsilon_t = \varepsilon_w$). At an elongation strain of 15% ($\varepsilon_l = 0.14$), the values of ε_t and ε_w should be 0.07. Measurement errors of ± 0.01 could lead to $R = 0.08/0.06 = 1.33$ or $R = 0.06/0.08 = 0.75$. Even if the accuracy were ± 0.002, the limits on R would be $0.072/0.068 = 1.06$ and $0.068/0.072 = 0.94$. Measurements of R at lower elongations are even less accurate.

The value of R often depends on the angle at which the specimen is cut from the sheet. In this case an average R-value, $\overline{R}$, is often quoted, where $\overline{R}$ is given by

$$\overline{R} = (R_0 + R_{90} + 2R_{45})/4 \tag{Eq 25}$$

The subscripts refer to the angles between the tensile axis and the rolling direction. $\overline{R}$ describes the degree of *normal anisotropy*, reflecting the difference between plastic properties in and normal to the plane of the sheet. Other properties are averaged in an analogous way. For example, for n and K in Eq 15,

$$\overline{n} = (n_0 + n_{90} + 2n_{45})/4 \tag{Eq 26}$$

and

$$\overline{K} = (K_0 + K_{90} + 2K_{45})/4 \tag{Eq 27}$$

The degree of anisotropy in the plane of the sheet *(planar anisotropy)* can be described by the parameter

$$\Delta R = (R_0 + R_{90} - 2R_{45})/2 \qquad\qquad (Eq\ 28)$$

The degree of earing in deep drawing correlates well with ΔR.

Measurement of Force

In the most modern tensile-testing machines, the force is measured by a load cell through which the force is applied. The load cell is built so that it will deform elastically under the loads applied. The amount of elastic deformation of the cell is sensed and converted to an electrical signal which in turn controls the movement of a pen and/or is displayed as a digital output. Often this is accomplished by mounting resistance strain gages on the load cell, although other methods may be used. In any case, the relation between the electric signal and force must be calibrated. In older hydraulic tensile machines, the force was measured by sensing the oil pressure, but this is no longer common.

Measurement of Strain

Several methods may be used to measure strain. With ductile polymers and metals, the deformation may be so large that strain can be calculated with sufficient accuracy from crosshead movement so that no direct measurements on the specimen itself are required. With screw-driven testing machines operating with a constant drive rate, the over-all crosshead movement can be deduced from time. If it is assumed that all of the crosshead displacement corresponds to elongation of the specimen, the engineering strain is simply the displacement divided by the length of the deforming region. This procedure neglects the fact that some of the crosshead movement corresponds to elastic distortion of the tensile machine and its grips and some to deformation of the shoulders of the specimen. The accuracy of this procedure can be increased by calibrating the loading system. An experiment must be run to determine the amount of displacement caused by the deformation of the machine, grips, and specimen shoulders as a function of load. This can then be subtracted from the total crosshead movement before dividing by the length of the deforming region.

For small strains, much greater accuracy can be achieved with an extensometer mounted directly on the specimen. An extensometer is a device designed specifically to measure small extensions by utilizing resistance strain gages, differential capacitors, or differential inductors to sense displacement. The changes in resistance, capacitance, or inductance are then converted to electrical signals which in turn can control a pen or chart-paper drive, or can be stored digitally in an output computer file.

Axial Alignment

It should be realized that, for strains in the elastic region, substantial errors may result from the use of a single extensometer unless the specimen is very straight and axially aligned. Both nonaxial loading and initial curvature of the specimen will have the same effect during loading (Fig 14). The reason for this is that the extensometer will respond to bending (or unbending) of the specimen as well as to its elongation. A bent specimen will tend to straighten as it is stretched. If the extensometer is on the outside of a bend, the straightening will cause a shortening of the extensometer and thus the extensometer will indicate too little extension. Likewise, an extensometer mounted on the inside of a bent specimen will indicate too much extension as the specimen is stretched. Nonaxiality thus can lead to appreciable error in measurement of elastic properties.

A simple way of compensating for nonaxiality is to measure strain with two strain gages mounted on opposite sides of the specimen. The total (or average) change recorded by the two gages will be independent of bending.

Axial alignment of the specimen is of particular concern in testing of brittle materials. Any nonaxiality will cause bending of the specimen and thus one side will be under a higher stress than the opposite side. In this case, the average stress (tensile force/cross-sectional area) will be lower than the stress on the more heavily loaded side. The measured (average) stress at fracture will be lower than the stress at the fracture site. Axiality can be improved by using soft material in the threads or under the grips. With low-carbon steels, nonaxial alignment may

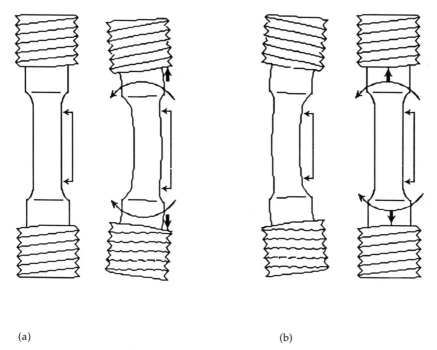

(a) (b)

Fig 14. Nonaxial loading can result from off-center loading (a) or initial curvature of the specimen (b). With bending caused by off-center loading (a), the strain measurement on the outside of the bend will be too large. The straightening of an initially bent specimen (b) will cause the strain measurement on the inside of the initial bend to be too large.

obscure the upper yield point. With ductile materials, nonaxiality is not a problem after the initial yielding, because the specimens will become straightened by the onset of plastic deformation.

Special Problems

With wire or rope, there is no simple way of using a reduction section. Instead, the continuous length is wrapped around drums, with friction between the drum and wire (or rope) providing the gripping action.

When specimens are tested at low or high temperatures, the entire gage section should be at the test temperature. For low-temperature testing, the specimen can be immersed in a constant-temperature liquid bath. For elevated temperatures, the specimen is usually surrounded by a controlled-temperature furnace. Under certain conditions, extraordinarily high (superplastic) elongations are observed at high temperatures. In these cases, elongations of 20-fold (2000%) or more have been found. With such large elongations, part of the gage section may be extended outside the constant-temperature region.

Summary

Tensile-test results depend on many arbitrary parameters of the testing procedure, including specimen geometry, strain rate, definitions of yielding, and methods of measurement. It is important, therefore, to state unambiguously the conditions of the test whenever test results are shared with others. Also, when possible, it is advisable to adhere to well-defined standards (e.g., ASTM standards).

Acknowledgments

The author wishes to thank A. Graf and D.J. Meuleman, who read the manuscript and made many valuable suggestions.

2

Tensile-Testing Equipment*

Tensile-testing equipment consists of several types of devices used to apply controlled tensile loads to test specimens. The equipment is capable of varying the speed of load application and accurately measuring the forces, strains, and elongations applied to the specimen.

Commercial tensile-testing equipment became available in the late 1800s. The earliest equipment used manual methods, such as hand cranks, to apply the load. In 1880, Tinius Olsen was granted a patent on the "Little Giant," a hand-cranked, 180 kN (40,000 lbf) capacity testing machine. In 1891, Olsen produced the first autographic machine

* This chapter is a revised, updated, and expanded version of the article "Tension Testing Machines and Extensometers," which appeared in Volume 8 of the 9th Edition of *Metals Handbook* (American Society for Metals, 1985). Special thanks are due to **Merrill A. Bishop** of MTS Systems Corporation and **James J. Martin** and **Kathy Hendry** of Instron Corporation for their help in revising this chapter.

capable of producing a stress-strain diagram (Ref 1). An example of an 1890 machine is shown in Fig 1.

Tensile-testing equipment has evolved from purely mechanical or electromechanical machines to sophisticated instruments that employ advanced electronics and microcomputers. This transition has made it possible to determine, rapidly and with great precision, values of ultimate tensile strength and elongation, yield strength, modulus of elasticity, and other material properties.

Tensile-testing machines apply uniaxial loading in a uniform manner and generally are universal in their capabilities and applications, rather than specific to one type of test or material. Therefore, the term

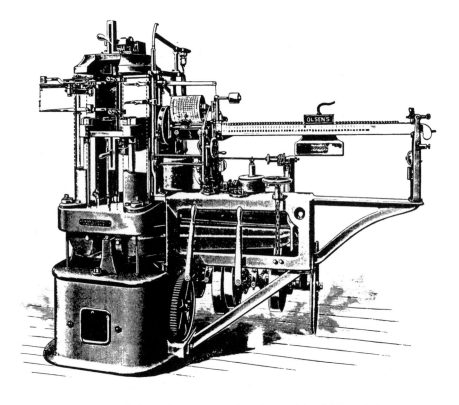

Fig 1. Screw-driven balance-beam universal testing machine (1890 model)

"*universal* testing system" is sometimes applied to such equipment, which can also perform compression, bending, and other types of tests.

Measurement of stresses and strains in a tensile tester typically is accomplished by using load- and strain-sensing transducers that create electrical signals proportional to the applied stresses or strains. The output of the transducer can be collected using manual or automated methods.

This chapter reviews the current technology of tensile testing equipment and examines the different types of equipment commercially available, including load- and strain-measurement techniques, specimen-gripping techniques, environmental (elevated- and low-temperature) equipment, and computerization of equipment.

Force-Application Systems

Most tensile tests are performed on electromechanical or servohydraulic test machines at strain rates of 10^{-5} to 10^{-2}/s. In electromechanical systems, the tensile forces are applied by a moving crosshead driven by a screw mechanism. In servohydraulic systems, the forces are created by a hydraulic actuation system.

Electromechanical Equipment

In an electromechanical testing system (more commonly called a screw-driven machine), the test load is applied through multiple drive screws and drive nuts that move a crosshead, which is attached to a grip holding one end of the test specimen. The other end of the specimen is attached by a grip to a fixed base. By driving of the screws at various rates, tensile tests can be conducted over a wide range of test conditions.

As shown in Fig 2, tensile forces are applied by a moving crosshead that is operated by two vertical lead screws. These are driven by a high-torque motor, typically powered by direct current (dc) for high starting torque, through either gears or belts. A closed-loop servodrive system ensures that the crosshead moves at a constant speed. Although the drive systems of individual units may differ, they essentially operate as follows.

The desired or user-selected speed and direction information is compared with a known reference signal. Positional control of the moving

Tensile Testing

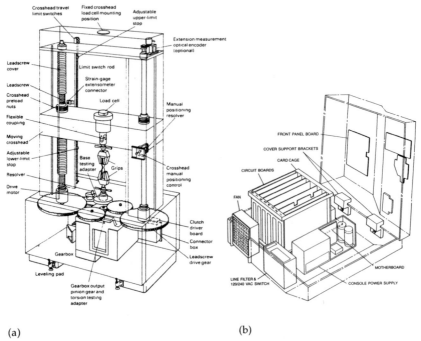

(a)   **(b)**

Fig 2. Components and controls for a screw-driven (electromechanical) tensile-testing machine. (a) Loading frame. (b) Control console

crosshead is controlled by the servomechanism to reduce any error or difference. This produces the desired crosshead speed. Direction and sequence of crosshead movement may be manually controlled using pushbuttons or automatic (computer) controls.

Because of the high forces involved, bearings and gears must meet precise tolerances in order to reduce friction and wear. Backlash, which is the free movement between the mechanical drive components, is particularly undesirable. Many instruments incorporate zero backlash drive trains so that forces are translated evenly through the lead screw and crosshead. These drive trains allow mechanical tests to be performed at full speed without any degradation in load capacity. Modern electromechanical systems generally are useful in ranges of up to 500 mm/min (20 in./min). Some can attain higher speeds, but the useful force available for application to the specimen drops as the speed of the crosshead motion increases.

State-of-the-art systems utilize precision optical encoders mounted directly on preloaded twin ball screws. These types of systems are capable of measuring crosshead displacement to an accuracy of 0.125% or better, with a resolution of 0.6 μm (100 μin.).

Servohydraulic Machines

Servohydraulic machines use hydraulic pressure in conjunction with an actuator to produce the desired specimen loading. These systems are capable of generating speeds and forces greater than those generated by electromechanical equipment. Servohydraulic systems also offer a much wider range of control and variation of applied specimen loading; tensile testing can be accomplished in load, strain, or displacement rate control. Other tests that can be performed using these systems include fatigue (da/dn and low-cycle fatigue) tests, fracture mechanics (K_{Ic} or J_{Ic}) tests, and simulated service loading tests on specimen coupons or components.

Because the response characteristics of a hydraulic cylinder under pressure are extremely fast, a servohydraulic system can quickly adapt to changing material characteristics such as specimen yielding or failure. This improves the accuracy of the property data that are generated.

A schematic diagram of a servohydraulic closed-loop system is shown in Fig 3. The servohydraulic testing system is a combination of hydraulic and electrical components. The primary hydraulic component within the loop is the actuator, which either extends or retracts as hydraulic pressure is applied to either side of the piston. A feedback transducer, such as a load cell, extensometer, or displacement transducer, converts the applied force, strain, or displacement into an electrical signal. The electronic portion of the system is the controller,

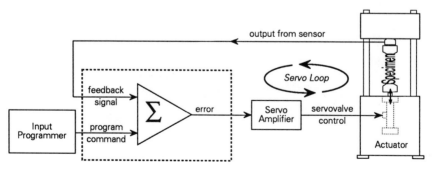

Fig 3. Schematic diagram of a basic servohydraulic closed-loop system

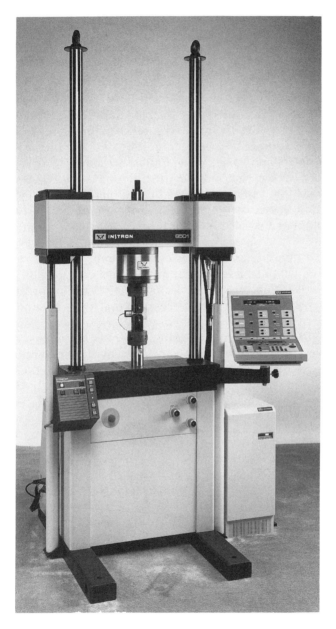

Fig 4. A servohydraulic tensile testing machine. Courtesy of Instron Corp.

which compares the command signal with actual conditions in the specimen and makes adjustments that drive the difference between the command and feedback signals to zero.

Servohydraulic test systems have the capability of testing at rates from as low as 45×10^{-11} m/s (1.8×10^{-9} in./s) up to 30 m/s (1200 in./s) or more. The actual useful rate for any particular system is dependent on the size of the actuator, the flow rating of the servovalve, and the noise level present in the system electronics. A typical servohydraulic system is shown in Fig 4.

Hydraulic actuators are available in a wide variety of force ranges. They are unique in their ability to provide economically forces as high as 4450 kN (1,000,000 lbf) or higher. Any completely mechanical testing system, such as the screw-driven machine described above, is limited in its ability to provide high forces because of problems associated with low machine stiffness and large and expensive loading screws, which are increasingly more difficult to produce as the force rating goes up.

Testing Machine Stiffness

The most common misconception relating to strain rate effects is that the testing machine is much stiffer than the specimen. Such an assumption leads to the concept of deformation of the specimen by an essentially rigid machine. However, for most tests the opposite is true: the conventional tensile specimen is much stiffer than most testing machines. The implications of testing machine stiffness are discussed in Ref 2; information is also available from testing machine manufacturers.

Load-Measurement Systems

The load- or force-measurement systems in tensile-testing machines typically employ strain-gage load cells or pressure-displacement transducers.

Strain-Gage Load Cells

Strain gages are devices that undergo electrical resistance changes in the presence of mechanical deformation (see the discussion of strain gages, below). A typical system uses a load cell connected to a bridge circuit to measure minute resistance changes and thus the applied loads or forces. The circuit is excited with a signal generated by the load-cell amplifier, and an applied force causes the strain-gage bridge circuit to be unbalanced. The resulting signal is returned to the amplifier, where

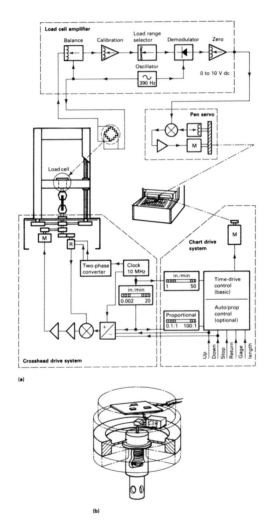

(a)

(b)

Fig 5. (a) Typical block diagram of a load-weighing system and (b) cross-sectional view of a load cell

it is amplified and converted into an output signal that is proportional to the applied force. The output can drive a digital display, a strip chart recorder, or a computer.

A load-cell amplifier enables the bridge circuit to compensate for different tare weights. It also includes a means of calibration, load-range selection, and zeroing adjustments that accommodate different load cells and load ranges. Figure 5 is a block diagram of a load-weighing system along with a cross-sectional view of a load cell, which is usually located in the machine crosshead.

Within individual load cells, mechanical stops can be incorporated so as to minimize the possible damage that could be caused by accidental overloads. Also, guides and supports can be included to prevent the deleterious effects of side loading and to provide the desired rigidity and ruggedness. This is important in tensile testing of metals because of the elastic recoil that can occur when a stiff specimen fails.

Pressure-Displacement Transducers

In pressure transducers, which are variations of strain-gage load cells, the strain-gaged member is activated by the hydraulic pressure of the system. The electrical circuits are the same in both cases.

Calibration

Calibration of load-measurement systems can be accomplished using precision weights, electrical calibration with factory-set standards, or proving rings. ASTM Standard E 4 (Ref 3) covers the load-verification procedure for tensile-testing machines.

Strain-Measurement Systems

Extensometers

Extensometers can be attached to a test specimen to measure elongation or strain as the load is applied. This is particularly important for metals and similar materials that exhibit high stiffness. Typical extensometers have fixed gage lengths, such as 25 or 50 mm (1 or 2 in.). They are also classified by maximum percent elongation so that a typical 25 mm (1 in.) gage-length unit would have different models for 10%, 50%, or 100% maximum strain. Schematics of two axial extensometers are shown in Fig 6.

There are also transverse strain-measurement devices that indicate the reduction in width or diameter as the specimen is tested. Averaging extensometers (Fig. 7) are also available for testing high-modulus materials. This type utilizes dual measuring elements that measure elongation on both sides of a specimen; the measurements are then averaged to obtain a mean strain.

Extensometers can use either linear variable differential transformers (LVDTs), which are electromechanical devices that provide an output voltage proportional to displacement, or strain gages such as those used in load cells, as described earlier.

LVDT extensometers are small, lightweight, and easy to use. Knife edges provide an exact point of contact and are mechanically set to the exact gage length. They can be fitted with breakaway features (Fig 8), sheet-metal clamps, low-pressure clamping arrangements, and other

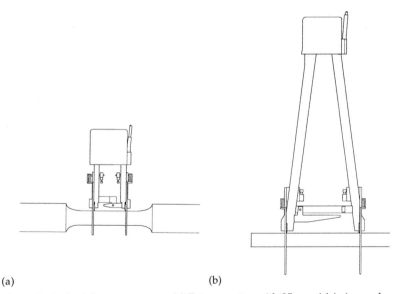

(a)   (b)

Fig 6. Typical axial extensometers. (a) Extensometer with 25 mm (1 in.) gage length and ± 3.75 mm (± 0.150 in.) travel suitable for static and dynamic applications with a variety of specimen geometries, dimensions, and materials. (b) Extensometer with 50 mm (2 in.) gage length and 25 mm (1 in.) travel suitable for large specimens and materials with long elongation patterns

Fig 7. A 50 mm (2 in.) gage-length breakaway-type LVDT extensometer that can remain on the specimen through rupture (Instron Corp).

Fig 8. Averaging axial extensometer mounted on a specimen. Courtesy of MTS Systems Corp.

35

devices. Thus, they can be used on small specimens, such as thread, yarn, and foil, and on large specimens, such as reinforcing bars, heavy steel plate, and tubing up to 75 mm (3 in.) in diameter.

Modifications of the LVDT extensometer described above permit linear measurements at both low and elevated temperatures (see the discussion on environmental chambers, below). Accurate measurements can also be made in vacuum.

Extensometers using strain gages rather than LVDTs are also available and are lighter in weight and smaller in size. The strain gage is usually mounted on a pivoting beam, which is an integral part of the extensometer. The beam is deflected by the movement of the extensometer knife edge when the specimen is stressed. The strain gage can be used to supply the information necessary to calculate strain, stress, angular torsion, and pressure.

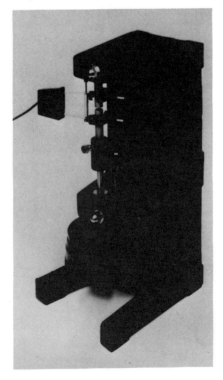

Fig 9. Strain-gage extensometer on precision calibration fixture. Courtesy of Instron Corp.

Basic types of strain gages include wire gages, foil gages, and capacitive gages. Wire and foil bonded resistance strain gages are used for measuring stress and strain and for calibration of load cells, pressure transducers, and extensometers.

For some strain measurements, strain gages are mounted directly on the test piece. More detailed information on these types of strain-gage applications can be found in the subsequent section on strain gages.

In conventional use, wire or foil strain gages, when mounted on test parts or structures for stress analysis, are discarded with the tested item. Foil strain gages are currently the most widely used, because of their ease of attachment.

The circuitry in the strain-measurement system allows multiple ranges of sensitivity, so one transducer can be used over a broad range. The magnification ratio, which is the ration of output to extensometer deflection, can be as high as 10,000 to 1. Extensometers are highly sensitive, but must be calibrated with precision micrometer-type fixtures to ensure accuracy. A strain-gage extensometer attached to a precision calibration fixture is shown in Fig 9. ASTM Standard E 83 describes the verification and classification of extensometers (Ref 4).

Optical systems featuring lasers can also be used to obtain linear strain measurements. Optical extensometers are particularly useful with materials such as rubber, thin films, plastics, and other materials where the weight of a conventional extensometer would distort the workpiece and affect the readings obtained.

Strain Gages (Ref 5)

The strain gage (Fig 10) is an extremely thin, small, strain-sensitive electrical resistor bonded to a flexible backing material that, when used as an integral part of an extensometer or load cell or when adhesively bonded to a test part or structure, transforms surface strains into changes in electrical resistance. The resulting changes in resistance are then read out directly as strain, load, pressure, torsion, and so forth, on the appropriate instrument.

Early bondable strain gages were manufactured by forming small-diameter (0.025 mm, or 0.001 in.) Constantan wire into a suitable grid geometry and bonding the grid in place on a paper carrier. The active gage lengths were relatively large, typically 6 mm (0.25 in.) or greater. Today, most precision strain gages are made by etching grids into thin metal foil held in place by a compatible backing. The active gage lengths vary from 0.2 to 100 mm (0.008 to 4.0 in.). Typical gage thickness for foil gages, including backing and grid, is 0.05 mm (0.002 in.) or less.

Gage Performance. Resistance strain gages are designed to measure strain in the axial direction of the grid (Fig 10) and to be as insensitive as possible to strains in the transverse direction. Because strain-gage grids tend to yield an integrated average of the strains under them, very short gages are generally used when the strain gradient is steep. Measuring strain over as small an area as possible tends to minimize any undesirable strain integration. Greater gage lengths are intended

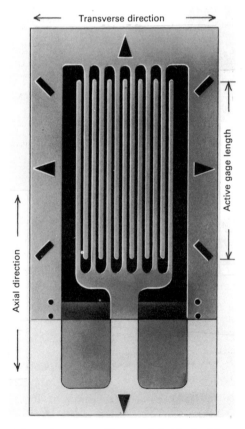

Fig 10. Modern foil strain gage with a polyimide backing and encapsulation. Magnification, approximately 6 ×.

for applications in which the mean strain over a considerable length is more representative. For example, gages with longer grids are commonly used on filament-wound composite test parts/structures to average out the strains in these non homogeneous materials consisting of filaments and matrix.

Gage sensitivity to strain is defined as the gage factor, *GF*, which is the ratio of unit change or resistance ($\Delta R/R$) to unit strain ($\Delta L/L$):

$$GF = \frac{\Delta R/R}{\Delta L/L} \tag{Eq 1}$$

The gage factor is a function of the gage design, as well as the alloy used to make the gage grid, its thermomechanical history, and, to a lesser degree, the measurement temperature. Gage factors at room temperature for most typical strain-gage alloys range from 2 to 4 (Table 1).

Grid Geometries. Because the grid of a strain gage is designed to measure normal strains in the axial direction of the grid, various gage geometries are used during strain measurement. Because gages with single grids measure strains in a single direction, their use should be restricted to well-defined uniaxial stress states—that is, pure tension or compression. When a measurement is required in a biaxial stress field and the directions of the principal strains are unknown or uncertain, a three-element strain-gage rosette (Fig 11a and 11b) should be used. With grids typically oriented at 0, 45, and 90°, or at 0, 60, and 120°, these gages enable three separate strain measurements to be made. When the principal axes are known, only two independent strain measurements are required. For these measurements, two-element "T" rosettes (Fig 11c)

Table 1. Compositions and gage factors (see Eq 1) for common strain-gage alloys

Material	Composition	GF
Advance or Constantan	45 Ni, 55 Cu	2.1
Karma	74 Ni, 20 Cr, 3 Al, 3 Fe	2.0
Isoelastic	36 Ni, 8 Cr, 0.5 Mo, 55.5 Fe	3.6
Nichrome V	80 Ni, 20 Cr	2.1
Platinum-tungsten	92 Pt, 8 W	4.0
Armour D	70 Fe, 20 Cr, 10 Al	2.0

Source: Ref 6

are used. Special-purpose gages for measuring shear strains are also available (Fig 11d).

Gage Materials. The gage user can choose from a variety of foil and backing materials that cover a wide range of performance and operating conditions. The most widely selected strain-sensing alloy for use on most materials is a copper-nickel alloy known as Constantan (Table 1). With a gage factor of about 2.1 for most grid geometries, Constantan can be thermomechanically processed to minimize the effects of thermally induced resistance changes (thermal output) that occur when gages undergo changes in temperature while strains are being

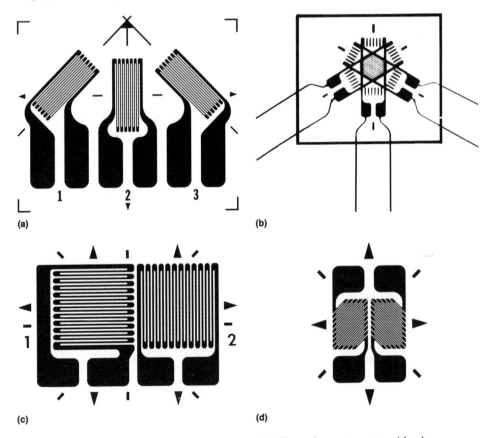

Fig 11. Typical strain-gage grid geometries. (a) Three-element rosette with planar construction. (b) Three-element rosette with stacked construction. (c) Two-element "T" rosette. (d) Two-element pattern for measuring shear strain.

measured. The measurement range of Constantan gages is generally limited to strains of 5% or less, except for gages made from fully annealed materials, which have a limit of 20%.

For elevated-temperature measurements—that is, up to 290 °C (550 °F) over a long term or 400 °C (750 °F) over a short term, a nickel-chromium alloy such as Karma (Table 1) is used for strain-gage grids. With a gage factor similar to that of Constantan, this alloy exhibits a higer fatigue life. The grids of gages having the greatest resistance to fatigue are made of an iron-nickel-chromium-molybdenum alloy called Isoelastic (see Table 1). This alloy has a high gage factor (about 3.5), but cannot be treated to minimize thermal effects. As a result, Isoelastic gages are normally used only in dynamic applications. The strain-measurement range of both Karma and Isoelastic gages is limited to strains of 2% or less. Isoelastic gages become very nonlinear at strains above 0.5%.

The strain-gage backing serves to hold the sensing grid in place. The backing (along with the adhesive) also electrically isolates the grid from the test specimen and transfers the strains from the surface of the test part to the sensing grid. For stress-analysis work, gage backings are commonly made of a tough, flexible polyimide. For extreme temperatures—that is, below −45 °C (−50 °F) or above 120 °C (250 °F)—a more stable glass-reinforced epoxy phenolic is commonly used.

The adhesive, which must transfer the strain from the specimen surface to the gage backing, is of paramount importance in gage installation. Specially qualified cyanoacrylate adhesives are popular because of their ease of application and short, room-temperature curing cycle. However, these adhesives are degraded by time, humidity, elevated temperatures, and moisture absorption. Under these conditions, an epoxy-base strain-gage adhesive would be a better selection. In addition to having higher elongation capabilities, epoxies have longer cure times. Some also require elevated-temperature cures.

Instrumentation. Modern strain-gage instruments generally employ a Wheatstone bridge as the primary sensing circuit. A stable, high-gain dc amplifier is then used to amplify the small bridge output signal to a level suitable for driving some form of display or output device. In addition to these two basic components, a typical strain indicator includes the bridge power supply and built-in bridge completion resistor, balance and gain controls, provisions for shunt calibration, and various convenience features.

Gripping Techniques

The use of proper grips and faces for tensile testing is critical in obtaining meaningful results. Trial and error often will solve a particular gripping problem. Grip manufacturers also can provide useful information and suggestions for proper grip selection. Tensile testing of most flat or round specimens can be accommodated with wedge-type grips (Fig 6). Wire and other types of specimens may require different grips, such as capstan or snubber types. The load capacities of grips range from under 45 N (10 lbf) to 450 kN (100,000 lbf) or more. ASTM Standard E 8 describes the various types of gripping devices used to transmit the measured load applied by the test machine to the tensile-test specimen (Ref 7).

The type of material to be tested often determines what gripping technique should be used. Refer to the chapters on tensile testing of specific material types for additional information about choosing the proper gripping technique.

Screw-Action Grips

Screw action or mechanical grips are low in cost and are available with load capacities of up to 4500 N (1000 lbf). This type of grip, which is normally used for testing of flat specimens, can be equipped with

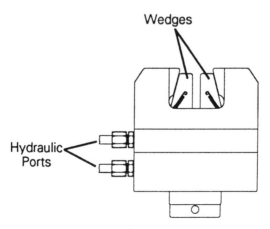

Fig 12. Schematic of a typical hydraulic wedge grip

interchangeable grip faces that come in a variety of surfaces. Faces are adjustable to compensate for different specimen thicknesses.

Wedge-Type Grips

Wedge-type grips are self-tightening and are built with capacities of up to 450 kN (100,00 lbf) or more. Some units can be tightened without altering the vertical position of the faces, making it possible to preselect the exact point at which the specimen will be held. The wedge-action design works well on hard-to-hold specimens and prevents the introduction of compressive forces that cause specimen buckling. Figure 12 is a schematic of a hydraulic wedge grip.

Pneumatic-Action Grips

Pneumatic-action grips are available in various designs with capacities of up to 900 N (200 lbf). This type of grip clamps the specimen by

Fig 13. A 50 mm (2 in.) gage-length averaging LVDT extensometer mounted on a threaded tensile specimen

lever arms that are actuated by compressed-air cylinders built into the grip bodies. A constant force maintained on the specimen compensates for decreases in force resulting from creep of the specimen in the grip. Another advantage of this design is the ability to optimize gripping force by adjusting the air pressure, which makes it possible to minimize specimen breaks at the grip faces.

Fig 14. Tensile-testing apparatus with environmental chamber for testing at up to 540 °C (1000 °F). Courtesy of Instron Corp.

Tensile-Testing Equipment

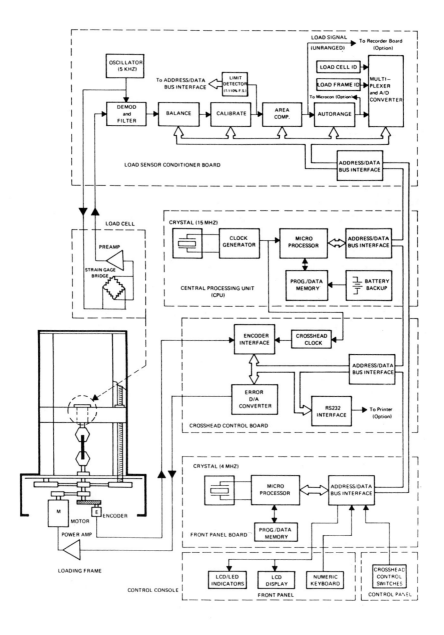

Fig 15. Block diagram of a computerized tensile-testing machine

Buttonhead Grips

Buttonhead grips permit rapid insertion of threaded-end (Fig 13) or mechanical-end specimens. They can be operated manually or pneumatically, as required by the type of material or test conditions.

Environmental Chambers

Elevated- and low-temperature tensile tests are conducted with basically the same specimens and procedures as those used for room-temperature tensile tests. However, the specimens must be heated or cooled in an appropriate environmental chamber (Fig 14). Also, the test fixtures must be sufficiently strong and corrosion resistant, and the strain-measuring system must be usable at the test temperature.

Strain gages are generally adequate between cryogenic temperatures and about 600 °C (1100 °F), but at higher temperatures, other devices must be used. Rod and tube extensometers, which are manufactured from a variety of materials, are most commonly used. When testing is done below room temperature, Teflon is suitable. Nickel-base superalloys are adequate for testing in air at up to 1100 °C (2010 °F). Above 1100 °C, ceramics are used in reactive atmospheres, whereas refractory metals are adequate for inert environments.

Environmental chambers contain automated systems for temperature control and can also simulate vacuum and high-humidity environments. Reference 8 describes environmental tensile testing in more detail.

Computerization

With current computer technology, it is possible to add a powerful data-reduction capability to a tensile testing machine, ranging from units that simply accept test results and perform minor calculations to large systems that control the complete testing-machine sequence, calculate test results, and store millions of bits of data. Besides providing accurate control, a computer provides flexibility in generating reports and in the storage and retrieval of test results.

Many manufacturers offer different computers with standardized software programs that are written to conform to ASTM or other test methods. By use of such programs, test functions such as machine control and data acquisition can be controlled by means of a keyboard/ mouse interface. Figure 15 illustrates how a test machine is connected to a computer through an interface that converts the analog load and strain data into digital data and presents them to the computer. Any control signals generated in the computer are transmitted to the test machine in a similar fashion.

One type of software package that is available allows the user to simply select the appropriate test from a predefined test method library; the computer can set all test conditions and limits automatically. Real-time test plots, complete with construction lines to show modulus, peak, break, and preset points, can be automatically displayed with calculated test results during the test. A predefined calculation library is available for report output, and additional calculations can be defined by the user. After testing, test results can be printed, plotted, sent to a network database, or sorted in the relational database

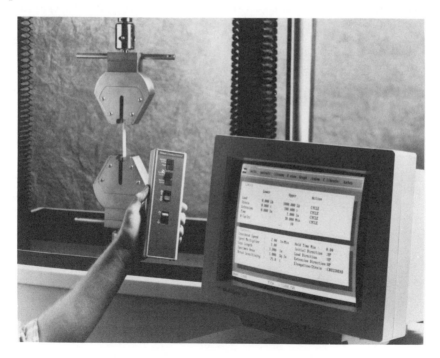

Fig 16. Computerized tensile-testing arrangement. Courtesy of Instron Corp.

for comparative analysis. Figure 16 shows an example of a computerized tensile-testing setup.

A computerized tensile-testing system eliminates manual interpretation of test curves, reducing human error and improving productivity. Detailed information on computer automation of materials testing can be found in Ref 9.

References

1. R.C. Clark, *Inspection of Metals, Volume II: Destructive Testing,* ASM International, 1988, p 83-87
2. P.P. Gillis and T.S. Gross, Effect of strain Rate on Flow Properties, *Metals Handbook,* Vol 8, 9th ed., American Society for Metals, 1985, p 38-46
3. "Standard Practice for Verification of Testing Machines," ASTM E 4, *Annual Book of ASTM Standards,* ASTM
4. "Standard Practice for Verification and Classification of Extensometers," ASTM E 83, *Annual Book of ASTM Standards,* ASTM
5. L.D. Lineback, Strain Measurement for Stress Analysis, *Metals Handbook,* Vol 17, 9th ed., ASM International, 1989, p 448-453
6. J.W. Dally and W.F. Riley, *Handbook on Experimental Mechanics,* Prentice-Hall, Inc., 1987, p 41-78
7. "Standard Methods of Tension Testing of Metallic Materials," ASTM E 8, *Annual Book of ASTM Standards,* ASTM
8. J.D. Whittenberger and M.V. Nathal, Elevated/Low Temperature Tension Testing, *Metals Handbook,* Vol 8, 9th ed., American Society for metals, 1985, p 34-37
9. B.C. Wonsiewicz, Ed., *Computer Automation of Materials Testing,* STP 710, ASTM, 1980

3

Test Methodology and Data Analysis

Paul M. Mumford, United Calibration Corporation

Sample Selection

When a material is tested, the objective usually is to determine whether or not the material is suitable for its intended use.

The sample to be tested must fairly represent the body of material in question. In other words, it must be from the same source and have undergone the same processing steps.

It is often difficult to match exactly the test samples to the structure made from the material. A common practice for testing of large

Tensile Testing

castings, forgings, and composite layups is to add extra material to the part for use as "built-in" test samples. This material is cut from the completed part after processing and is made into test specimens that have been subjected to the same processing steps as the bulk of the part.

In practice, these specimens may not exactly match the bulk of the part in certain important details, such as the grain patterns in critical areas of a forging. One or more complete parts may be sacrificed to obtain test samples from the most critical areas for comparison with the "built-in" samples. Thus, it may be determined how closely the "built-in" samples represent the material in question.

There is a special case in which the object of the test is to evaluate not the material, but the test itself. Here, the test specimens must be as nearly identical as possible so the differences in the test results represent, as far as possible, only the variability in the testing process.

Sample Preparation

It should be remembered that a "sample" is a quantity of material that represents a larger lot. The sample usually is made into multiple "specimens" for testing. Test samples must be prepared properly to achieve accurate results. The following rules are suggested for general guidance.

First, as each sample is obtained, it should be identified as to material description, source, location and orientation with respect to the body of material, processing status at the time of sampling, and the data and time of day that the sample was obtained.

Second, test specimens must be made carefully, with attention to several details. The specimen axis must be properly aligned with the material rolling direction, forging grain pattern, or composite layup. Cold working of the test section must be minimized. The dimensions of the specimen must be held within the allowable tolerances established by the test procedure. The attachment areas at each end of the specimen must be aligned with the axis of the bar (see Fig 1). Each specimen must be identified as belonging to the original sample. If total elongation is to be measured after the specimen breaks, the gage length must be marked on the reduced section of the bar prior to testing.

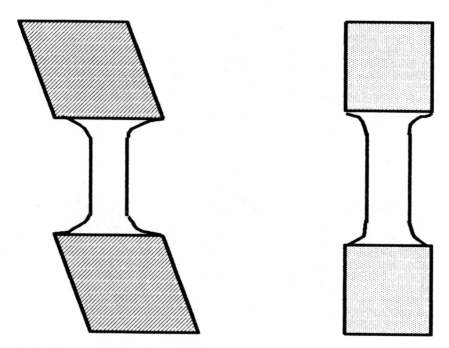

Fig 1. Improper (left) and proper (right) alignment of specimen attachment areas with axis of specimen

Test Set-Up

The test set-up requires that equipment be properly matched to the test at hand. There are three requirements of the testing machine: force capacity sufficient to break the specimens to be tested; control of test speed (or strain rate or load rate), as required by the test specification; and precision and accuracy sufficient to obtain and record properly the load and extension information generated by the test. This precision and accuracy should be ensured by current calibration certification.

For grips, of which many types are in common use in tensile testing, only two rules apply: the grips must properly fit the specimens (or vice versa), and they must have sufficient force capacity so that they are not damaged during testing.

There are several techniques for installing the specimen in the grips. With wedge grips, placement of the specimen in the grips is critical to proper alignment (see Fig 2). Ideally, the grip faces should be of the

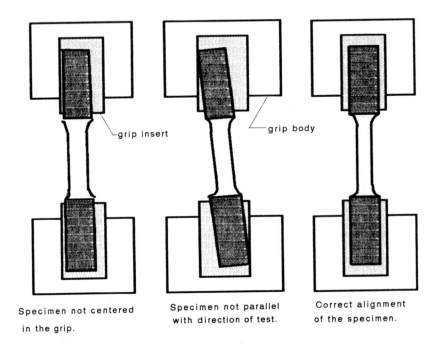

Specimen not centered in the grip.

Specimen not parallel with direction of test.

Correct alignment of the specimen.

Fig 2. Improper (left, center) and proper (right) alignment of specimen in grips

same width as the tab ends of the test bar; otherwise, lateral alignment is dependent only on the skill of the technician. The wedge grip inserts should be contained within the grip body or crosshead, and the specimen tabs should be fully engaged by the grips (see Fig 3).

Other types of grips have perhaps fewer traps for the inexperienced technician, but an obvious one is that, with threaded grips, a length of threads on the specimen equal to at least one diameter should be engaged in the threaded grips.

There are several potential problems that must be watched for during the test set-up, including specimen misalignment and worn grips. The physical alignment of the two points of attachment of the specimen is important, because any off-center loading will exert bending loads on the specimen. This is critical in testing of brittle materials, and may cause problems even for ductile materials. Alignment will be affected by the testing-machine loadframe, any grips and fixtures used, and the

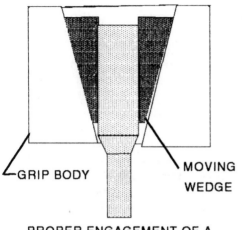

GRIP BODY

MOVING
WEDGE

PROPER ENGAGEMENT OF A
SPECIMEN IN WEDGE GRIPS.

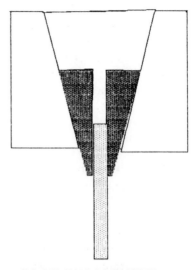

POOR ENGAGEMENT.
THIS SMALL "BITE" IS
LIKELY TO CAUSE DAMAGE
TO THE GRIPS, AND
RISK OF INJURY TO
ANYONE NEAR THE
MACHINE.

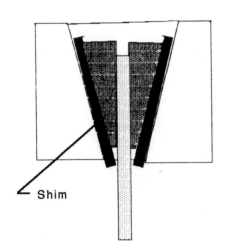

Shim

Fig 3. Proper and improper engagement of a specimen in wedge grips

specimen itself. Misalignment may also induce load-measurement errors due to the passage of bending forces through the load-measuring apparatus. Such errors may be reduced by the use of spherical seats or "U-joints" in the set-up.

Worn grips may contribute to off-center loading. Uneven tooth marks across the width of the specimen tab are an indication of trouble in wedge grips. Split-collar grips may also cause off-center loading. Uneven wear of grips and mismatching of split-shell insert pairs are potential problem areas.

Strain measurements are required for many tests. They are commonly made with extensometers, but strain gages are frequently used—especially on small specimens or where Poisson's ratio is to be measured. If strain measurements are required, appropriate strain-measuring instruments must be properly installed. The technician should pay particular attention to setting of the extensometer gage length (mechanical zero). The zero of the strain readout should repeat consistently if the mechanical zero is set properly. In other words, once the extensometer has been installed and zeroed, subsequent installations should require minimal readjustment of the zero.

Test Procedure

The following general rules for test procedure may be applied to almost every tensile test.

Load and strain ranges should be selected so that the test will fit the range. The maximum values to be recorded should be as close to the top of the selected scale as convenient without running the risk of going past full scale. Ranges may be selected using past experience for a particular test, or specification data for the material (if available). Note that many computer-based testing systems have automatic range selection and will capture data even if the range initially selected is too small.

The identity of each specimen should be verified, and pertinent identification should be accurately recorded for the test records and report.

The dimensions needed to calculate the cross-sectional area of the reduced section should be measured and recorded. These measurements

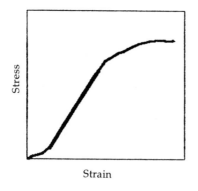

Extensometer located on the inside of a
curved specimen.

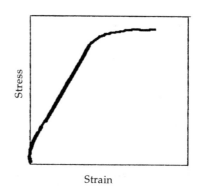

Extensometer located on the outside of a
curved specimen.

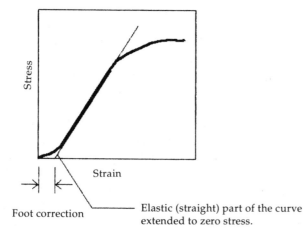

Fig 4. Stress-strain curves showing evidence of extensometer being located on inside
and outside of a curved specimen, and demonstrating "foot correction"

should be repeated for every specimen; it should not be assumed that
sample preparation is perfectly consistent.

The load-indicator zero and the plot-load-axis zero, if applicable,
should be set before the specimen is placed in the grips. Zeroes should
never be reset after the specimen is in place.

Tensile Testing

The specimen is placed in the grips and is secured by closing the grips. If preload is to be removed before the test is started, it should be physically unloaded by moving the loading mechanism. The zero adjustment should never be used for this purpose. Note that, in some cases, preload may be desirable and may be deliberately introduced. For materials for which the initial portion of the curve is linear, the strain zero may be corrected for preload by extending the initial straight portion of the stress-strain diagram to zero load and measuring strain from that point. The strain valve at the zero-load intercept is commonly called the "foot correction" and is subtracted from readings taken from strain scale (see Fig 4).

When the extensometer, if applicable, is installed, the technician should be sure to set the mechanical zero correctly. The strain-readout zero should be set after the extensometer is in place on the specimen.

The test procedure should be in conformance with the published test specification and should be repeated consistently for every test. It is important that the test specification be followed for speed of testing. Some materials are sensitive to test speed, and different speeds will give different results. Also, many testing-machine load- and strain-measuring instruments are not capable of responding fast enough for accurate recording of test results if an excessive test speed is used.

The technician should monitor the test closely and be alert for problems. One common sign of trouble is a load-versus-strain plot in which the initial portion of the curve is not straight (see Fig 4). This may indicate off-center loading of the specimen, improper installation of the extensometer, or the specimen was not straight to begin with.

Another potential trouble sign is a sharp drop in indicated load during the test. Such a drop may be characteristic of the material, but it also can indicate problems such as slippage between the specimen and the grips or stick-slip movement of the wedge grip inserts in the grip body. Slippage may be caused by worn inserts with dull teeth, particularly for hard, smooth specimens.

The stick-slip action in wedge grips is more common in testing of resilient materials, but it also can occur in testing of metals. Specimens cut from the wall of a pipe or tube may have curved tab ends that flatten with increasing force, allowing the inserts to move relative to the grip body. Short tab ends on round specimens also may be crushed by the wedge grips, with the same result. If the sliding faces are not lubricated, they may move in unpredictable steps accompanied by drops in the load reading. Dry-film molybdenum disulfide lubricants are effective in solving stick-slip problems in wedge grips, particularly when testing is done at elevated temperature.

When wedge grips are used, the specimen must be installed so that the clamping force is contained within the grip body. Placing the specimen too near the open end of the grip body results in excessive stress on the grip body and inserts and is a common cause of grip failure. WARNING: Grip failures are dangerous and may cause injury to personnel and damage to equipment.

Data

Data generally may be grouped into "raw data," meaning the observed readings of the measuring instruments, and "calculated data," meaning the test results obtained after the first step of analysis.

In the most simple tensile test, the raw data comprise a single measurement of peak force and the dimensional measurements taken to determine the cross-sectional area of the test specimen. The first analysis step is to calculate the "tensile strength," defined as the force per unit area required to fracture the specimen. More complicated tests will require more information, which typically takes the form of a graph of force versus extension. Computer-based testing machines can display the graph without paper, and can save the measurements associated with the graph by electronic means.

A permanent record of the raw test data is important, because it allows additional analyses to be performed later, if desired, and because it allows errors in analysis to be found and corrected by reference to the original data.

Data Recording

Test records may be needed by many departments within an organization, including metallurgy, engineering, commercial, and legal departments.

Engineering and metallurgy departments typically are most interested in material properties, but may use raw data for error checking or additional analyses. The metallurgy department wants to know how variations in raw materials or processing change the properties of the product being produced and tested, and the engineering department wants to know the properties of the material for design purposes.

Shipping, receiving, and accounting departments need to know whether or not the material meets the specifications for shipping, acceptance, and payment. The sales department needs information for advertising and for advising prospective customers.

If a product incorporating the tested material later fails—particularly if persons are injured—the legal department may need test data as evidence in legal proceedings. In this case, a record of the raw data will be important for support of the original analysis and test report.

Reporting

The test report usually contains the results of tests performed on one sample composed of several specimens.

When ASTM specifications are used for testing, the requirements for reporting are defined by the specification. The needs of a particular user probably will determine the form for identification of the material, but the reported results will most likely be as given in the ASTM test specification.

The information contained in the test report generally should include identification of the testing equipment, the material tested, and the test procedure; the raw and calculated data for each specimen; and a brief statistical summary for the sample.

Each piece of test equipment used for the test should be identified, including serial numbers, capacity or range used, and date of certification or date due for certification.

Identification of the material tested should include the type of material (alloy, part number, etc.); the specific batch, lot, order, heat, or coil from which the sample was taken; the point in the processing sequence (condition, temper, etc.) at which the sample was taken; and any test or pretest conditions (test temperature, aging, etc.).

Identification of the test procedure usually will be reported by reference to a standard test procedure such as those published by ASTM or perhaps to a proprietary specification originating within the testing organization.

The raw data for each specimen are recorded, or a reference to the raw data is included so that the data can be obtained from a file if and when they are needed. Frequently, only a portion of the raw - data—dimensions, for example—is recorded, and information on the force-versus-extension graph is referenced.

A tabulation of the properties calculated for each specimen is recorded. The calculations at this stage are the first level of data analysis. The calculations required usually are defined in the test procedure or specification.

A brief statistical summary for the sample is a feature that is becoming more common with the proliferation of computerized testing systems, because the computations required can be done automatically without added operator workload. The statistical summary may include the average (mean) value, median value, standard deviation, highest value, lowest value, range, etc. The average or median value would be used to represent this sample at the next level of analysis, which is the material database.

Examination of this initial statistical information can tell a great deal about the test as well as the material. A low standard deviation or range indicates that the material in the sample has uniform properties (each of several specimens has nearly the same values for the measured properties) and that the test is producing consistent results. Conversely, a high standard deviation or range indicates that a problem of inconsistent material or testing exists and needs to be investigated.

A continuing record of the average properties and the associated standard deviation and range information is the basis for statistical process control, which systematically interprets this information so as

Table 1 Cross-reference to tensile testing standards for selected materials

Material	ASTM	International Organization for Standardization (ISO)	British Standard (BS)	Japanese Industrial Standard (JIS)
Metals..................	E 8	6892	10 002	Z2241
Elastomers...........	D 412	37	903.A2	K6301
Plastics	D 638	527	2782	K7113
Composites..........	D 3039	3268	2747	K7054
Adhesives.............	D 1002	4587, 6922	5350	K6849

to provide the maximum information about both the material and the test process.

Table 1 lists selected ASTM and international tensile test standards.

Analysis

Analysis of test data is done at several levels. First, the technician observes the test in progress, and may see that a grip is slipping or that the specimen fractures outside the gage section. These observations may be sufficient to determine that a test is invalid.

Immediately after the test, a first-level analysis is performed according to the calculation requirements of the test procedure. ASTM test specifications typically show the necessary equations with an explanation and perhaps an example. This analysis may be as simple as dividing peak force by cross-sectional area, or it may require more complex calculations. The outputs of this first level of analysis are the mechanical properties of the material being tested.

Upon completion of the group of tests performed on the sample, a statistical analysis may be made. The statistical analysis produces average (mean or median) values for representation of the sample in the subsequent database and also provides information about the uniformity of the material and the repeatability of the test.

The results of tests on each sample of material may be stored in a database for future use. The database allows a wide range of analyses to be performed using statistical methods to correlate the mechanical-properties data with other information about the material. For example, it may allow determination of whether or not there is a significant difference between the material tested and similar material obtained from a different supplier or through a different production path.

4

Tensile Testing of Metals and Alloys

M.R. Louthan, Jr. Materials Technology Section,
Savannah River Laboratory

The tensile test provides a relatively easy, inexpensive technique for developing mechanical-property data for the selection, qualification, and utilization of metals and alloys in engineering service. This data may be used to establish the suitability of the alloy for a particular application, to measure the conformance of the alloy with specifications, and/or to provide a basis for comparison with other candidate

materials. Design guidelines generally require that the tensile properties of metals and alloys meet specific, well-defined criteria. ASME has
established code requirements for the strengths and ductilities of many
classes of metals and alloys. Step-by-step procedures for conducting
the tensile test are defined by ASTM standards. Descriptions of the
importance of both material and test variables on the measured tensile
properties are available in the *ASM Handbook*. Because such variables
have significant influences on the measured tensile properties, an understanding of these influences is necessary for the accurate interpretation and use of most tensile data.

The elastic moduli of cast iron, carbon steel, and many other engineering materials are dependent on the rate at which the test specimen
is stretched (strain rate). The yield strength or stress at which a specified amount of plastic strain takes place is also dependent on the test
strain rate. Alloy composition, grain size, prior deformation, test temperature and heat treatment may also influence the measured yield
strength. Generally, factors that increase the yield strength decrease the

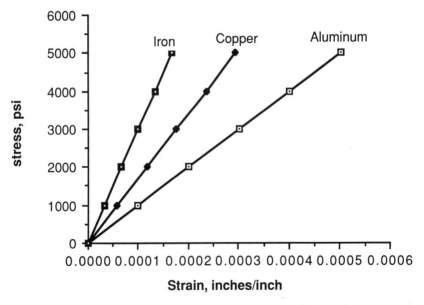

Fig 1. Schematic representation of the elastic portions of the stress-strain curves for
iron, copper, and aluminum

tensile ductility because these factors also inhibit plastic deformation. However, a notable exception to this trend is the increase in ductility that accompanies an increase in yield strength when the grain size is reduced.

Most structural metals and alloys, when strained to failure in a tensile test, fracture by ductile processes. The fracture surface is formed by the coalescence or combination of microvoids. These microvoids generally nucleate during plastic deformation processes, and co-alescence begins after the plastic deformation processes become highly localized. Strain rate, test temperature, and microstructure influence the coalescence process and, under selected conditions (decreasing temperature, for example), the fracture may undergo a transition from ductile to brittle processes. Such transitions may limit the utility of the alloy and may not be apparent from strength measurements. The tensile test, therefore, may require interpretation, and interpretation requires a knowledge of the factors that influence the test results. This chapter provides a metallurgical perspective for such interpretation.

Elastic Behavior

Most structures are designed so that the materials of construction undergo elastic loadings under normal service conditions. These loads produce elastic or reversible strains in the structural materials. The upward movement of a wing as an airplane takes off and the sway of a tall building in a strong wind are examples in which the elastic strains are readily apparent. Bending of an automobile axle and stretching of a bridge with the passing of a car are less noticeable examples of elastic strains. The magnitude of the strain is dependent on the elastic moduli of the material supporting the load. Although elastic moduli are not generally determined by tensile testing, tensile behavior can be used to illustrate the importance of elastic properties in the selection and use of metals and alloys.

Young's modulus for iron (207 GPa, or 30×10^6 psi) is approximately three times that of aluminum (69 GPa, or 10×10^6 psi) and almost twice that of copper (117 GPa, or 17×10^6 psi). This variation in elastic behavior is illustrated in Fig 1. Because of its higher value of Young's modulus, an iron component will deflect less than an "identical" copper or aluminum component that undergoes an equivalent load. In a tensile test, for example, the elastic tensile strains in 12.8 mm (0.505 in.) diam tensile bars of iron, copper, and aluminum loaded to 455 kg (1000 lb) will be 1.6×10^{-4} mm/mm (in./in.) for iron, 2.9×10^{-4} mm/mm (in./in.) for copper, and 5×10^{-4} mm/mm (in/in) for aluminum.

These strains are calculated from the following equations:

$$A = \pi D^2 / 4$$

$$\sigma = L/A$$

$$\sigma = E \varepsilon$$

(See the chapter "Overview of Tensile Testing" for the development of the equations and the definition of the symbols used).

The ability of a material to resist elastic deformation is termed "stiffness," and Young's modulus is one measure of that ability. Engineering applications that require very rigid structures, such as microscopes, antennas, satellite dishes, and radio telescopes, must be constructed from either very massive components or selected materials that have high values of elastic moduli. The elastic modulus of iron is higher than those of many metals and alloys, and thus iron and iron alloys are frequently used for applications that require high stiffness.

The equation that defines Young's modulus, $\sigma = E \varepsilon$, is based on the observation that tensile strain is linearly proportional to the applied stress. This linear relationship provides an adequate description of the behavior of metals and alloys under most practical situations. However, when materials are subjected to cyclic or vibratory loading, even slight departures from truly linear elastic behavior may become important. One measure of the departure from linear elasticity is the anelastic response of a material.

Anelasticity

Anelasticity is time-dependent, fully reversible deformation. The time dependence results from the lack of instantaneous atom movement during the application of a load. There are several mechanisms for time-dependent deformation processes, including the diffusive motion of alloy and/or impurity atoms. This diffusive motion may simply be atoms jumping to nearby lattice sites made favorable by the application of a load.

Tensile loading of an iron-carbon alloy will produce elastic strains in the alloy, and its body-centered-cubic structure will be distorted to become body-centered-tetragonal. Carbon, in solid solution, produces a similar distortion of the iron lattice. There is one basic difference between the distortions introduced by tensile loads and those introduced by dissolving carbon. The average distortion of a metallic lattice during a tensile test is anisotropic: each unit cell of the structure is elongated in the direction of the tensile load and, because of Poisson's ratio, the material also contracts in the lateral direction. In contrast, the average lattice distortion resulting from the solution of carbon is isotropic

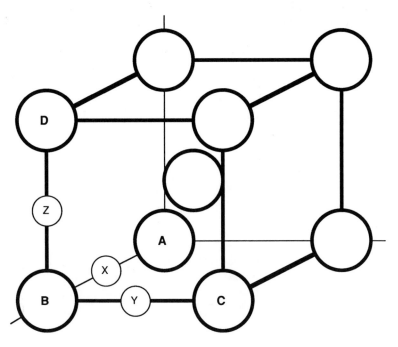

Fig 2. Interstitial sites in an iron lattice. The large spheres at the corners and center of the cube represent iron atoms, and the small spheres (X, Y, and Z) represent interstitial sites for carbon. There are duplicate interstitial sites at the corners of the cube or unit cell

even though each individual carbon atom produces a localized anisotropic distortion.

Carbon atoms, in solid solution in iron, are located at the interstitial
sites shown schematically in Fig 2. Because the dissolved carbon atoms
are too big for the interstitial sites, a carbon atom at site X would push
the iron atoms A and B apart and cause the unit cell to elongate in the
x direction. Similarly, a carbon atom at site Y would push iron atoms B
and C apart and cause elongation in the y direction, and a carbon atom
at site Z would cause elongation in the z direction. Within any given
unstressed iron or alpha grain, carbon atoms are randomly distributed
in X, Y, and Z sites. Thus, although each unit cell is distorted in one
specific direction, the over-all distortion of the unstressed grain is
basically isotropic, or equal in all directions.

The application of a tensile stress causes specific interstitial sites to
be favored. If the tensile stress is parallel to the x direction, type X sites
are expanded and become favored sites for the carbon atoms. Type Y
sites become favored if the stress is in the y direction, and type Z sites

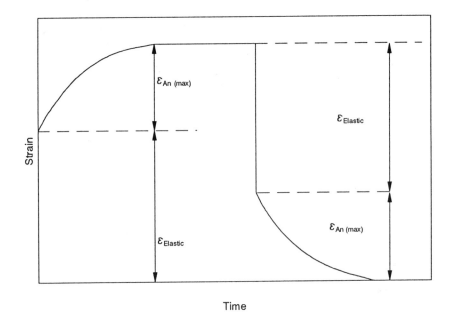

Fig 3. A relationship between elastic and anelastic strains. The elastic strains develop
as soon as the load is applied, whereas the anelastic strains are time dependent

are favored when stresses are in the z direction. During a tensile test, carbon atoms will migrate or diffuse to the sites made favorable by the application of the tensile load. This migration is time and temperature dependent and can be the cause of anelastic deformation.

The sudden application of the tensile load may elastically strain the iron lattice at such a high rate that carbon migration to favored sites cannot occur as the load is applied. However, if the material remains under load, the time-dependent migration to favored sites will produce additional lattice strain because of the tendency for the interstitial carbon to push iron atoms in the direction of the applied stress. These additional strains are the anelastic strains in the material. Similarly, if the load is suddenly released, the elastic strains will be immediately recovered whereas recovery of the anelastic strains will require time as the interstitial carbon atoms relocate from the previously favorable

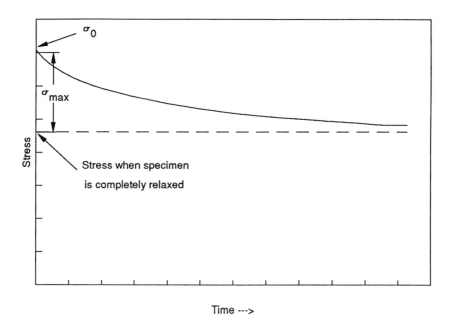

Time --->

Fig 4. The elastic aftereffect. The tensile specimen was loaded to a stress of σ_0 and then held. The time-dependent drop in stress results from a decrease in the load required to maintain a fixed displacement. This decrease results from anelastic strains that increase the length of the test specimen. When the anelastic straining process is complete, the stress has relaxed by a value of σ_{max}.

sites to form a uniform distribution in the iron lattice. The time dependence of the elastic and anelastic strains is shown schematically in Fig 3.

The combination of the elastic and anelastic strains may cause Young's modulus, as determined in a tensile test, to be loading-rate (or strain-rate) dependent and may produce damping or internal friction in a metal or alloy subjected to cyclic or vibratory loads. Anelastic strains are one cause of stress relaxation in a tensile test when the test specimen is loaded and held at a fixed displacement. This stress relaxation is frequently called an "elastic aftereffect" and results in a time-dependent load drop because the load necessary to maintain the fixed displacement will decrease as atoms move to favored sites and anelastic deformation takes place. This elastic aftereffect, illustrated in Fig 4, demonstrates the importance of time or loading rate on test results.

The total reversible strain that accompanies the application of a tensile load to a test specimen is the sum of the elastic and anelastic strains. Rapid application of the load will cause the anelastic strain to approach zero (the test time is not sufficient for anelastic strain), thus

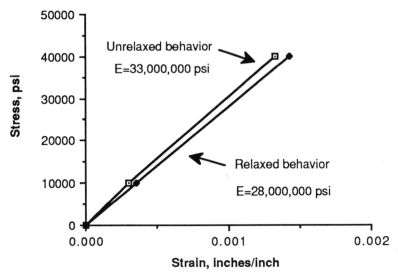

Fig 5. Loading-rate effects on Young's modulus

the total strain during loading will equal the true elastic strain. Very slow application of the same load will allow the anelastic strain to accompany the loading process, thus the total reversible strain in this test will exceed the reversible strain during rapid loading. The measured value of Young's modulus in the low-strain-rate test will be lower than that measured in the high-strain-rate test, and the measured modulus of elasticity will be strain-rate dependent. This dependency is illustrated in Fig 5. The low value of Young's modulus is termed the "relaxed modulus", and the modulus measured at high strain rates is termed the "unrelaxed modulus".

Damping

Tensile tests and cyclic loadings frequently are made at strain or loading rates that are intermediate between those required for fully relaxed behavior and those required for fully unrelaxed behavior.

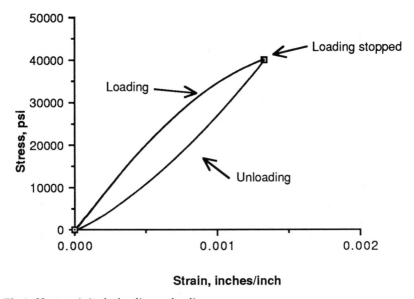

Fig 6. Hysteresis in the loading-unloading curve

Therefore, on either loading or unloading, the initial or short-time portion of the stress-strain curve will produce unrelaxed behavior whereas the later, longer-time portions of the curve will produce more relaxed behavior. The transition from unrelaxed to relaxed behavior produces a loading-unloading hysteresis in the stress-strain curve (Fig 6).

This hysteresis represents an energy loss during the load-unload cycle. The amount of energy loss is proportional to the magnitude of the hysteresis. Such energy losses that may be attributed to anelastic effects within the metal lattice are termed "internal friction." Internal friction plays a major role in the ability of a material to absorb vibrational energy. Such absorption may cause the temperature of a material to rise during the loading-unloading cycle. One measurement of the susceptibility of a material to internal friction is the damping capacity. Because anelasticity and internal friction are dependent on time and temperature, the damping capacity of a metal or alloy is both temperature and strain-rate dependent.

Internal friction and damping play major roles in the response of a metal or alloy to vibrations. Materials tested under conditions that cause significant internal friction during loading-unloading cycles undergo large energy losses and are said to have high damping capacities. Such materials are useful for the absorption of vibrations. Cast iron, for example, has a very high damping capacity and is frequently used for the bases of instruments and equipment that must be isolated from room vibrations. Lathes, presses, and other pieces of heavy machinery also use cast iron bases to minimize transmission of machine vibrations to the floor and surrounding area. However, a high damping capacity is not always a useful material quality. Bells, for example, are constructed from materials with low damping capacities because both the length of bell ring and the loudness of the tone will increase as the damping capacity decreases.

Anelasticity, damping, stress relaxation, and the elastic moduli of most metals and alloys are dependent on the microstructure of the material as well as on test conditions. These properties are not typically determined by tensile-testing techniques. However, these properties, as well as the machine parameters, influence the shape of the stress-strain curve. Therefore, an awareness of these phenomena may be useful in the interpretation of tensile-test data.

The Proportional Limit

The apparent stress necessary to produce the onset of curvature in the tensile stress-strain relationship is the proportional limit. The *ASM Metals Reference Book* defines the proportional limit as the maximum stress at which strain remains directionally proportional to stress. Departures from proportionality may be attributed to anelasticity and/or the initiation of plastic deformation. The ability to detect the occurrence of these phenomena during a tensile test is dependent on the accuracy with which stress and strain are measured. The measured value of the proportional limit decreases as the accuracy of the measurement increases (Fig 7). Because the measured value of proportional limit is dependent on test accuracy, the proportional limit is not generally reported as a tensile property of metals and alloys. Furthermore, values of proportional limit have little or no utility in the selection,

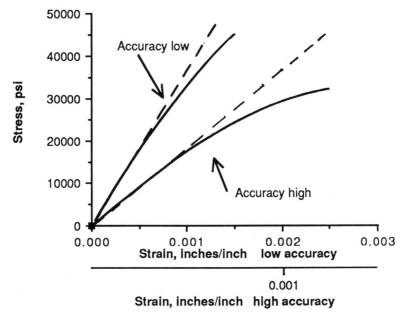

Fig 7. Effect of accuracy of measurement on the determination of the proportional limit

qualification, and use of metals and alloys for engineering service. A far more reproducible and practical stress is the yield strength of the material.

Yielding and the Onset of Plasticity

The yield strength of a metal or alloy may be defined as the stress at which that metal or alloy exhibits a specified deviation from the proportionality between stress and strain. Very small deviations from proportionality may be cause by anelastic effects, but these departures from linear behavior are fully reversible and do not represent the onset of significant plastic (nonreversible) deformation or yielding. Theoretical values of yield strength, σ_{Thero}, are calculated from equations such as

$$\sigma_{Thero} = \frac{E}{2\pi}$$

Based on these calculations, yielding should not take place until the applied stress is a significant fraction of the modulus of elasticity, These estimates for yielding generally overpredict the measured yield strengths by factors of at least 100, as summarized in Table 1.

The discrepancy between the theoretical and actual yield strength results from the motion of dislocations. Dislocations are defects in the crystal lattice, and the motion of these defects is a primary mechanism of plastic deformation in most metals and alloys.

Table 1. Young's modulus and theoretical and measured yield strengths of selected metals at 20 °C (68 °F)

| Metal | Young's modulus | | Yield strength | | | |
| | | | Theoretical | | Measured* | |
	GPa	10^6 psi	GPa	10^6 psi	Mpa	ksi
Aluminum	70.3	10.2	11	1.6	26	4
Nickel	199	28.9	32	4.6	234	34
Silver	82.7	12.0	13	1.9	131	19
Steel (mild)	212	30.7	34	4.9	207	30
Titanium	120	17.4	19	2.7	172	25

*Measured values of yield strength are dependent on the metallurgical condition of the material.

There are three very broad categories of crystal defects in metallic solids:

1. Point defects, including vacancies and alloy or impurity atoms

2. Line defects of dislocations

3. Area defects, including grain and twin boundaries, phase boundaries, inclusion-matrix interfaces, and even external surfaces

The characterization of these defects in any particular material may be accomplished through metallography. Optical metallography is used to characterize area defects or grain structure, as shown in Fig 8.

Transmission electron microscopy is used to characterize line defects or dislocation substructure, as shown in Fig 9. More specialized metallographic techniques, such as field ion microscopy, are used to characterize the point defects. Interaction among defects is common, and most

Fig 8. Optical photomicrograph of type 304 stainless steel. The apparent defects include grain boundaries, twin boundaries, and inclusions. 100 ×

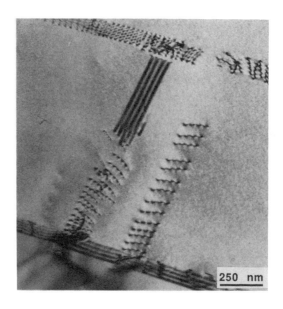

(a)

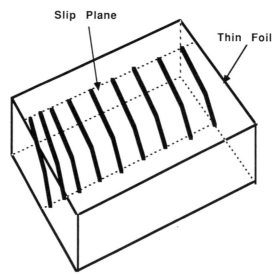

(b)

Fig 9. (a) Transmission electron micrograph of type 304 stainless steel showing dislocation pileups at an annealing twin boundary. (b) Schematic representation of dislocations on a slip plane

techniques that alter the yield strengths of metals and alloys are dependent on defect interactions to alter the ease of dislocation motion.

Dislocation mobility is dependent on the alloy content, the extent of cold work, the size, shape, and distribution of inclusions and second phase particles, and the grain size of the alloy. The strength of most metals increases as alloy content increases, because the alloy (or impurity) atoms interact with dislocations and inhibit subsequent motion. Thus, this type of strengthening results from the interaction of point defects with line defects. Such strengthening was discovered by ancient metallurgists and was the basis for the Bronze Age. The strength, and therefore the utility, of copper was significantly increased by dissolving tin to form bronze. The yield strength of the copper-tin alloys (bronze) was sufficiently high for the manufacture of tools and spear points. This strengthening mechanism was not discovered by the native Americans, and on the American Continents, copper was used for jewelry but not for more practical purposes. Bronzes (Cu-Sn alloys), brasses (Cu-Zn alloys), monels (Ni-Cu alloys), and many other alloy systems are dependent on solid-solution strengthening to control the yield strength of the material. The effects of nickel and zinc additions on the yield strength of copper are illustrated in Fig 10.

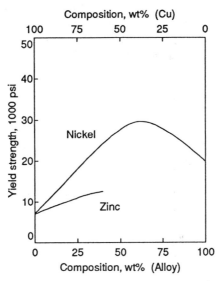

Fig 10. Effects of nickel and zinc contents on the yield strengths of copper alloys

Cold work is another effective technique for increasing the strength of metals and alloys. This strengthening mechanism is effective because the number of dislocations in the metal increases as the percentage of cold work increases. These additional dislocations inhibit the continued motion of other dislocations in much the same manner as increased traffic decreases the mobility of cars along a highway system. Cold work is an example of strengthening because of line defects interacting with other line defects in a crystal lattice. Many manufactured components depend on cold work to raise their strength to the required level. Rolling, stamping, forging, drawing, swaging, and even extrusion may be used to provide the necessary cold work. The effects of cold work on the hardness and strength of a 70%Cu-30%Zn alloy, iron and copper are illustrated in Fig 11. The yield and tensile strengths follow nearly identical trends, with the yield strength increasing slightly faster than the tensile strength.

Grain and phase boundaries also block dislocation motion. Thus, the yield strength of most metals and alloys increases as the number of grain boundaries increases and/or as the percentage of second phase in the structure increases. A decrease in the grain size increases the number of grain boundaries per unit volume, thus increasing the density of area defects in the metal lattice. Because interactions between area defects and line defects inhibit dislocation mobility, the yield strengths of most metals and alloys increase as the grain size decreases and as the number of second-phase particles increases. The effects of grain size are illustrated in Fig 12. Because of these and other strengthening mechanisms,

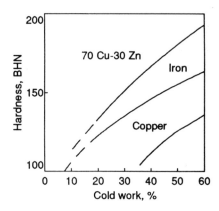

Fig 11. Effects of cold work on the hardnesses and strengths of brass, iron, and copper

any given alloy may show a wide range of yield strengths. The range will be dependent on the grain size, percentage of cold work, distribution of second-phase particles, and other relatively easily quantified, microstructural parameters. The values of these microstructural parameters depend on the thermomechanical history of the material; thus a knowledge of these very important metallurgical variables is almost a necessity for intelligent interpretation of yield-strength data and for the design and utilization of metallic structures and components.

The most common definition of yield strength is the stress necessary to cause a plastic strain of 0.002 mm/mm (in./in.). This strain represents a readily measurable deviation from proportionality, and the stress necessary to produce this deviation is the 0.2% offset yield strength (see the chapter "Overview of Tensile Testing" for a detailed description of the 0.2% offset yield strength). A significant amount of dislocation motion is required before a 0.2% deviation from linear behavior is reached. Therefore, in a standard tensile test, the 0.2% offset yield strength is almost independent of test-machine variables, gripping effects and reversible nonlinear strains such as anelasticity. Because of this independence, the 0.2% offset yield strength is a reproducible material property that may be used in the characterization of the mechanical properties of metals and alloys. However, it is vital to realize that the magnitude of the yield strength, or any other tensile property, is dependent on the defect structure of the material tested. Therefore, the thermomechanical history of the metal or alloy must be known if yield strength is to be a meaningful design parameter.

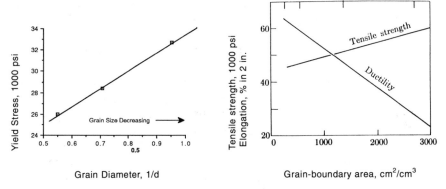

Fig 12. Schematic illustrations of the effects of grain size on the strengths and ductilities of metals and alloys

The Yield Point

The onset of dislocation motion in some alloys, particularly low-carbon steels tested at room temperature, is sudden, rather than a relatively gradual process. This sudden occurrence of yielding makes the characterization of yielding by a 0.2% offset method impractical. Because of the sudden yielding, the stress-strain curve for many mild steels has a yield point, and the yield strength is characterized by lower yield stress. The yield point develops because of interactions between the solute (dissolved) atoms and dislocations in the solvent (host) lattice. The solute-dislocation interaction in mild steels involves carbon migration to and interaction with dislocations. Because the interaction causes the concentration of solute to be high in the vicinity of the dislocations, the yield point is said to develop because of segregation of carbon to the dislocations.

Many of the interstitial sites around dislocations are enlarged and are therefore low-energy or favored sites for occupancy by the solute atoms. When these enlarged sites are occupied, a high concentration or atmosphere of solute is associated with the dislocation. In mild steels, the solute segregation produces carbon-rich atmospheres at dislocations. Motion of the dislocations is inhibited because such motion requires the separation of the dislocations from the carbon atmospheres. As soon as the separation takes place, the stress required for continued dislocation motion decreases and, in a tensile test, the lower yield strength is reached. This yielding process involves dislocation motion in localized regions of the test specimen. Because dislocation motion is plastic deformation, the regions in which dislocations moved represent deformed regions or bands in the metal. These localized, deformed bands are called Lüders bands. Once initiated, additional strain causes the Lüders bands to propagate throughout the gage length of the test specimen. This propagation takes place at a constant stress which, is the lower yield strength of the steel. When the entire gage section has yielded, the stress-strain curve begins to rise because of the interaction of dislocations with other dislocations, and strain-hardening initiates.

The existence of a yield point and Lüders band is particularly important because of the impact of the sudden softening and localized straining on processing techniques. For example, sudden localized yielding will cause jerky material flow. Jerky flow is undesirable in a drawing operation because the load on the drawing equipment would change rapidly, causing large energy releases that must be absorbed by the processing equipment. Furthermore, localized Lüders strains will produce stretch marks in stamped materials. These strech marks are termed "stretcher strains" and are readily apparent on stamped surfaces. This impairs the surface appearance and reduces the utility of the component. If materials that do not have yield points are stamped, smooth surfaces are developed because the strain-hardening process spreads the deformation uniformly throughout the material. Uniform, continuous deformation is important in many processing and finishing operations; thus, it is important to select a combination of material-processing conditions that minimize the tendency toward localized yielding.

Grain-Size Effects on Yielding

The metals and alloys used in most structural applications are polycrystalline. The typical metallic object contains tens of thousands of microscopic crystals or grains. The size of the grains is difficult to define precisely because the 3-D shape of the grain is quite complex. If the grain is assumed to be spherical, the grain diameter, d, may be used to characterize size. More precise characterizations of grain size include the mean grain intercept, $\bar{l}$, and the ratio of grain-boundary surface to grain volume, S_v. These two parameters may be established through quantitative metallographic techniques. The grain structure of the metal or alloy of interest is examined at a magnification, X, and a line of a known length l is overlaid on the microstructure. The number of grain-boundary intersections with that line in measured, divided by the length of the line, and multiplied by the magnification. The resulting parameter, N_l, is the average number of grain boundaries intersected per unit length of line. This value for N_l is related to $\bar{l}$ and S_v through

$$\bar{l} = 1/N_l$$

and

$$S_v = 2N_l$$

Tensile Testing

Unfortunately, for historical reasons, the parameter d is the most common measure used to characterize the influence of grain size on the yield strengths of metals and alloys. This influence is frequently quantified through the Hall-Petch relationship whereby yield strength, σ_y, is related to grain size through the empirical equation

$$\sigma_y = \sigma_0 + kd^{-1/2}$$

The empirical constants σ_0 and k are the lattice friction stress and the Petch slope, respectively. A graphical representation of this relationship is shown in Fig 12.

Grain boundaries act as barriers to dislocation motion, causing dislocations to pile up behind the boundaries. This pileup of dislocations concentrates stresses at the tip of the pileup, and when the stress is sufficient, additional dislocations may be nucleated in the adjacent grain. The magnitude of the stress at the tip of a dislocation pileup is dependent on the number of dislocations in the pileup. The number of dislocations that may be contained in a pileup increases with increasing grain size because of the larger grain volume. This difference in the number of dislocations in a pileup makes it easier for new dislocations to be nucleated in a large-grain metal than in a fine-grain metal of comparable purity, and this difference in the ease of dislocation nucleation extrapolates directly to a difference in yield strength. Based on this

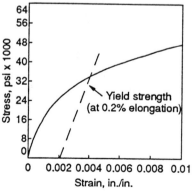
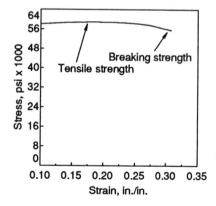

Fig 13. Stress-strain curve for nickel.

model for grain-size strengthening, the effects of grain size should exist even after the yield strength is exceeded.

Strain Hardening and the Effect of Cold Work

A stress-strain curve for relatively pure nickel (Fig 13) shows that the 0.2% offset yield strength of this metal was approximately 235 MPa (34 ksi). The stress necessary to cause continued plastic deformation increased as the tensile strain increased. After a strain of approximately 1%, the stress necessary to produce continued deformation was 330 MPa (48 ksi), and after 10% strain the necessary stress had increased to approximately 415 MPa (60 ksi).

The stress necessary for continued deformation is frequently designated as the flow stress at that specific tensile strain. Thus, at 1% strain, the flow stress is 330 MPa (48 ksi), and the flow stress at 10% strain is 415 MPa (60 ksi). This increasing flow stress with increasing strain is the basis for increasing the strength of metals and alloys by cold working. The effects of grain size on the strength of the alloy are retained throughout the cold working process (Fig 14).

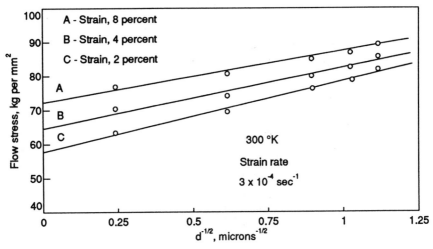

Fig 14. Effects of grain size and cold work on the flow stress of titanium

81

The fact that the grain-size dependence of strength is retained throughout the strain-hardening process demonstrates the possibility for interactions among the various strengthening mechanisms in metals and alloys. For example, cold work causes strength increases through the interaction between point defects and dislocations, and these effects are additive to the effects of alloying. This is apparent in Fig 15(a), where the incremental increase in strength resulting from zinc additions to copper becomes larger when the alloy is cold worked.

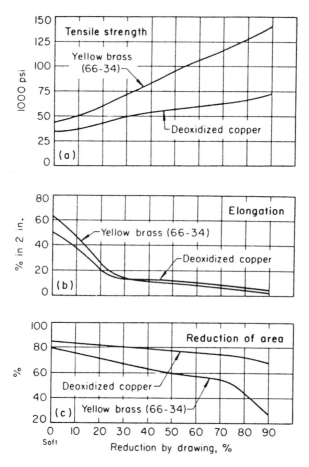

Fig 15. Effects of cold work on the tensile properties of copper and yellow brass. (a) Tensile strength. (b) Elongation. (c) Reduction in area

Furthermore, strength is not the only tensile property affected by the cold working process. Ductility decreases with increasing cold work

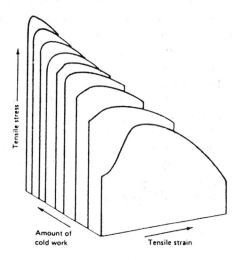

Fig 16. Effects of cold work on the tensile stress-strain curves of low-carbon steel bars

Fig 17. Effect of cold rolling on grain shape in cartridge brass. (a) Grain structure in annealed bar. (b) Grain structure in same bar after 50% reduction by rolling. Diagram in the lower left of each micrograph indicates orientation of the view relative to the rolling plane of the sheet. 75×.

(Fig 15b and c), and, if cold working is too extensive, metals and alloys will crack and fracture during the working operation. The over-all effects of cold work on strength and ductility are illustrated in Fig 16, which compares the tensile behavior of steel rods that were cold drawn various amounts before being tested to fracture.

Note that the increase in strength and decrease in ductility cause the area under the stress-strain curve to decrease. This is significant because that area represents the work or energy required to fracture the steel bar, and the tensile-test results demonstrate that this energy decreases as the percentage of cold work increases.

Cold working, whether by rolling, drawing, stamping, or forging, changes the microstructure. The resulting grain shape is determined by the direction of metal flow during processing, as illustrated in Fig 17. The grains in the cold rolled specimen were elongated and flattened, thus changing from the semispherical grains in Fig 17(a) to the pancake-shape

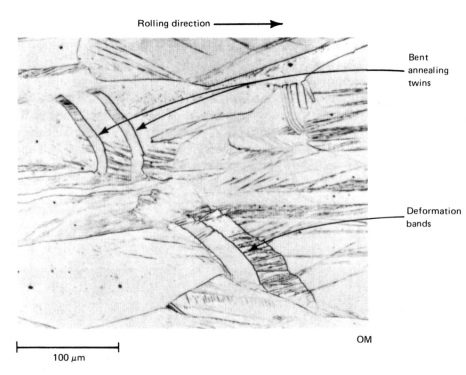

Rolling direction ⟶

Bent annealing twins

Deformation bands

OM

100 μm

Fig 18. Grain structure of severely deformed copper alloy

grains in Fig 17(b). A rod-drawing process would have produced needle-shape grains in this same alloy. In addition to the changes in grain shape, the grain interior is distorted by cold forming operations. Bands of high dislocation density (deformation bands) develop, twin boundaries are bent, and grain boundaries become rough and distorted (Fig 18). Because the deformation-induced changes in microstructure are anisotropic, the tensile properties of wrought metals and alloys frequently are anisotropic. The strain-hardened microstructures and the associated mechanical properties that result from cold work can be significantly altered by annealing. The microstructural changes that are introduced by heating to higher temperatures are dependent on both the time and temperature of the anneal. This temperature dependence is illustrated in Fig 19 and results because atom motion is required for the anneal to be effective.

The sudden drop in hardness seen in the Cu-5%Zn alloy results from recrystallization, or the formation of new grains, in the alloy.

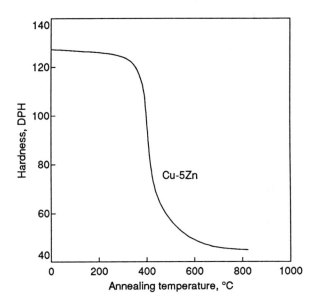

Fig 19. Effect of annealing on hardness of cold rolled Cu-5%Zn brass. Hardness can be correlated with strength, and the strengths of this alloy would show similar annealing effects

Tensile Testing

Plastic deformation of metals and alloys at temperatures below the recrystallization temperature is cold work, and plastic deformation at temperatures above the recrystallization temperature is hot work. Metals and alloys, in tensile tests above the recrystallization temperature, do not show significant strain hardening, and the tensile yield strength becomes the maximum stress that the material can effectively support.

Ultimate Strength

The ability to strain harden is one of the general characteristics in mechanical behavior that distinguish metals and alloys from most other engineering materials. Not all metallic materials exhibit this characteristic. Chromium, for example, is very brittle and fractures in a tensile test without evidence of strain hardening. The stress-strain curves for these brittle metals are similar to those of most ceramics (Fig 20). Fracture occurs before significant plastic deformation takes place.

Such brittle materials have no real yield strength, and the fracture stress is the maximum stress that the material can support. Most metals and alloys, however, undergo plastic deformation prior to fracture, and the maximum stress that the metal can support is appreciably higher

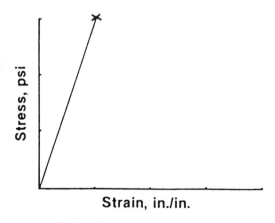

Fig 20. Stress-strain curve for brittle material

than the yield strength. This maximum stress (based on the original dimensions) is the ultimate or tensile strength of the material.

The margin between the yield strength and the tensile strength provides an operational safety factor for the use of many metals and alloys in structural systems. Other than this safety margin, the actual value of tensile strength has very little practical use. The ability of a structure to withstand complex service loads bears little relationship to tensile strength, and structural designs must be based on yielding.

Tensile strength is easy to measure and is frequently reported because it is the maximum stress on an engineering stress-strain curve. Engineering codes may even specify that a metal or alloy meet some tensile-strength requirement. Historically, tensile strengths, with experience-based reductions to avoid yielding, were used in design calculations. As the accuracy of measurement of stress-strain curves improved, utilization of tensile strength diminished, and by the 1940s most design guidelines were based on yielding. There is a large empirical database that correlates tensile strength with hardness, fatigue strength, stress rupture, and mechanical properties. These correlations, historical code requirements, and the fact that structural designs incorporating brittle materials must be based on tensile strength provide the technical basis for the continuing utilization of tensile strengths as design criteria.

Cold work and other strengthening mechanisms for metals and alloys do not increase tensile strength as rapidly as they increase yield strength. Therefore, as evident in Fig 16, strengthening processes frequently are accompanied by a reduction in the ability to undergo plastic strain. This reduction decreases the ability of the material to absorb energy prior to fracture and, in many cases, is important to successful materials utilization. Analysis of the tensile behavior of metals and alloys can provide insight into the energy-absorbing abilities of the material.

Toughness

The ability to absorb energy without fracturing is related to the toughness of the material. Most, if not all, fractures of engineering materials are initiated at pre-existing flaws. These flaws may be small enough to be elements of the microstructure or, when slightly larger,

Tensile Testing

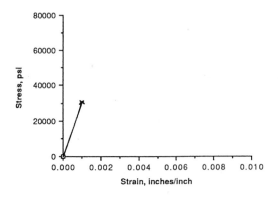

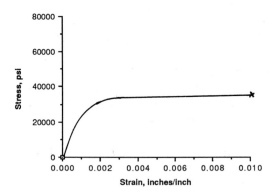

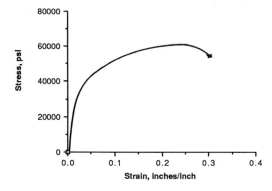

Fig 21. Stress-strain curves for materials showing various degrees of plastic deformation or ductility

may be macroscopic cracks in the material or, in the extreme, visually observable discontinuities in the structure. A tough material resists the propagation of flaws through processes such as yielding and plastic deformation. Most of this deformation takes place near the tip of the flaw. Because fracture involves both tensile stress and plastic deformation, or strain, the stress-strain curve can be used to estimate material toughness. However, there are specific tests designed to measure material toughness. Most of these tests are conducted with precracked specimens and include both impact and fracture-mechanics type studies (see *Metals Handbook*, Volume 8, for descriptions of these tests). Toughness calculations based on tensile behavior are estimates and should not be used for design.

The area under a stress-strain curve (normalized to specimen dimensions) is a measure of the energy absorbed by the material during a tensile test. From that standpoint, this area is a rough estimate of the toughness of the material. Because the plastic strain associated with tensile deformation of metals and alloys is typically several orders of magnitude greater than the accompanying elastic strain, plasticity or dislocation motion is very important to the development of toughness. This is illustrated by the stress-strain curves for a brittle, a semibrittle, and a ductile material shown schematically in Fig 21.

Brittle fracture (see Fig 21a), takes place with little or no plastic strain, and thus the area under the stress-strain curve, A is given by

$$A = (1/2)\sigma\varepsilon$$

and, because all the strain is elastic,

$$\sigma = E\varepsilon$$

Combining these equations gives

$$A = (1/2) \, (\sigma_f^2)E$$

where σ_f is the fracture stress. If the fracture stress for this material were 205 MPa (30 ksi) and Young's modulus were 205 GPa (30×10^6 psi), the fracture energy, estimated from the stress-strain curve, would be 1.2×10^{-3} J/mm^3 (15 lbf · in./in.^{3}) per cubic inch of gage section in the test specimen. If the test specimen were ductile (Fig 21c), the area under the stress-strain curve could be estimated from

$$A = (\sigma_y + \sigma_t)(\varepsilon_f/2)$$

where σ_y is yield strength, σ_t is tensile strength, and ε_f is strain to fracture. Estimation of the fracture energy from the typical tensile properties of mild steel test specimens, σ_y = 205 MPa (30 ksi), σ_t = 415 MPa (60 ksi), and ε_f = 0.3, gives 1.12 J/mm³ (13,500 lbf · in./in.³) of gage section in the test specimen.

The ratio of the energy for ductile fracture to the energy for brittle fracture is 900. This ratio is based on the calculations shown above and will increase with increasing strain to fracture and with increasing strain hardening. These area and energy relationships are only approximations. The stresses used in the calculations are based on the original dimensions of the test specimen. The utility of such toughness estimates is the ease with which testing can be accomplished and the insight that the estimates provide into the importance of plasticity to the prevention of fracture. This importance is illustrated by considering the area under the stress-strain curve shown in Fig 21(b). Assuming that, for this semibrittle material, the yield strength and tensile strength are both 205 MPa (30 ksi,) (no significant strain hardening) and that

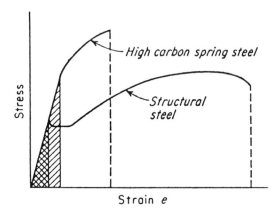

Fig 22. Comparison of the stress-strain curves for high- and low-toughness steels.

fracture takes place after a plastic strain of only 0.01 mm/mm (in./in.), the area under the stress-strain curve is 410 J (300 lbf · in.) per unit area. This area is 20 times higher than the area under the stress-strain curve for brittle fracture shown in Fig 21(a). This calculation demonstrates that a plastic strain of only 0.01% can have a remarkable effect on the ability of a material to absorb energy without fracturing.

Toughness is a very important property for many structural applications. Ship hulls, crane arms, axles, gears, couplings, and airframes are all required to absorb energy during service. The ability to withstand earthquake loadings, system overpressures, and even minor accidents will also require material toughness. Increasing the strength of metals and alloys generally reduces ductility and, in many cases, reduces toughness. This observation illustrates that increasing the strength of a material may increase the probability of service-induced failure when material toughness is important for satisfactory service. This is seen by comparing the areas under the two stress-strain curves in Fig 22.

The cross-hatched regions in Fig 22 illustrate another tensile property—the modulus of resilience, which can be measured from tensile stress-strain curves. The ability of a metal or alloy to absorb energy through elastic processes is the resilience of the material. The modulus of resilience is defined as the area under the elastic portion of the stress-strain curve. This area is the strain energy per unit volume and is equal to

$$A = (1/2)(\sigma_y^2/E)$$

Increasing the yield strength and/or decreasing Young's modulus will increase the modulus of resilience and improve the ability of a metal or alloy to absorb energy without undergoing permanent deformation.

Ductility

Material ductility in a tensile test is generally established by measuring either the elongation to fracture or the reduction in area at fracture. George

E. Dieter, in his classic book *Mechanical Metallurgy*, states that "In general, measurements of ductility are of interest in three ways:

1. To indicate the extent to which a metal can be deformed without fracture in metal working operations such as rolling and extrusion.

2. To indicate to the designer, in a general way, the ability of the metal to flow plastically before fracture. A high ductility indicates that the material is 'forgiving' and likely to deform locally without fracture should the designer err is stress calculation or the prediction of severe loads.

3. To serve as an indicator of changes in impurity level or processing conditions. Ductility measurements may be specified to assess material quality even though no direct relationship exists between the ductility measurement and performance."

Tensile ductility is therefore a very useful measure in the assessment of material quality. Many codes and standards specify minimum values for tensile ductility. One reason for these specifications is the assurance of adequate toughness without the necessity of requiring a more costly toughness specification. Most changes in alloy composition and/or processing conditions will produce changes in tensile ductility. The

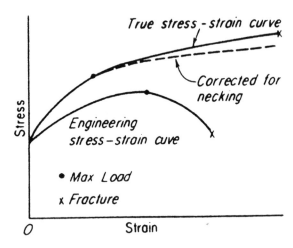

Fig 23. Comparison of engineering and true stress-strain curves

"forgiveness" found in many metals and alloys results from the ductility of these materials. Although there is some correspondence between tensile ductility and fabricability, the metalworking characteristics of metals and alloys are better correlated with the ability to strain harden than with the ductility of the material. The strain-hardening abilities of many engineering alloys have been quantified through the analysis of true stress-strain behavior.

True Stress-Strain Relationships

Conversion of engineering stress-strain behavior to true stress-strain relationships may be accomplished using the techniques represented by Eq 8 through 14 in Chapter 1. This conversion, summarized graphically in Fig 23, demonstrates that the maximum in the engineering stress-strain curve results from tensile instability, not from a decrease in the strength of the material. The drop in the engineering stress-strain curve is artificial and occurs only because stress calculations are based on the original cross-sectional area. Both testing and analysis show that, for most metals and alloys, the tensile instability corresponds to the onset of necking in the test specimen. Necking results from strain localization; thus, once necking is initiated, true strain cannot be calculated from specimen elongation. Because of these and other analytical limitations of engineering stress-strain data, if tensile data are used to understand and predict metallurgical response during the deformation associated with fabrication processes, true stress–true strain relationships are preferred.

The deformation that may be accommodated, without fracture, in a deep drawing operation varies with the material. For example, austenitic stainless steels may be successfully drawn to 50% reductions in area whereas ferritic steel may fail after only 20 to 30% reductions in area in similar drawing operations. Both types of steel will undergo in excess of 50% reduction in area in a tensile test. This difference in drawability correlates with the strain-hardening exponent (n from an equation of the form $\sigma_t = K\varepsilon_t^n$ or $\sigma_t = K\varepsilon_t^n + \Delta$) and therefore is apparent from the slope of the true stress–strain curves for the two alloys (Fig 24).

The strain-hardening exponents, or n values for ferritic and austenitic steels, are typically 0.25 and 0.5, respectively. A perfectly plastic material would have a strain-hardening exponent of zero and a completely elastic solid would have a strain-hardening exponent of one. Most metals and alloys have strain-hardening exponents between 0.1 and 0.5. Strain-hardening exponents correlate with the ability of dislocations to move around or over dislocations and other obstacles in their path. Such movement is termed "cross slip." When cross slip is easy, dislocations do not pile up behind each other and strain-hardening exponents are low. Mild steels, aluminum, and some nickel alloys are examples of materials that undergo cross slip easily. The value of n increases as cross slip becomes more difficult. Cross slip is very difficult in austenitic stainless steels, copper, and brass and the strain-hardening exponent for these alloys is approximately 0.5.

Tensile specimens, sheet or plate material, wires, rods, and metallic sections have spot-to-spot variations in section size, yield strength, and other microstructural and structural inhomogeneities. Plastic deformation of these materials initiates at the locally weak regions. In the absence of strain hardening, this initial plastic strain would reduce the net section size and focus continued deformation in the weak areas. Strain hardening, however, causes the flow stress in the deformed region to increase. This increase in flow stress increases the load necessary for continued plastic deformation in that area and causes the deformation to spread throughout the section. The higher the strain-hardening exponent, the greater the increase in flow stress and the greater the tendency for plastic deformation to become uniform. This

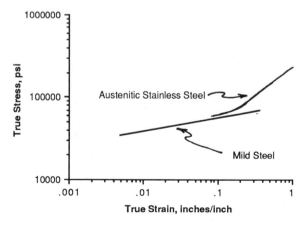

Fig 24. True stress-strain curves for austenitic and mild steels

tendency has a major impact on the fabricability of metals and alloys. For example, the maximum reduction in area that can be accommodated in a drawing operation is equal to the strain-hardening exponent as determined from the true stress-strain behavior of the material. Because of such correlations, the effects of process variables such as strain rate and temperature can be evaluated through tensile testing. This provides a basis to approximate the effects of process variables without direct, in-process assessment of the variables.

Temperature and Strain-Rate Effects

The yield strengths of most metals and alloys increase as the strain rate increases and decrease as the temperature increases. This strain–rate temperature dependence is illustrated in Fig 25. These dependencies result from a combination of several metallurgical effects.

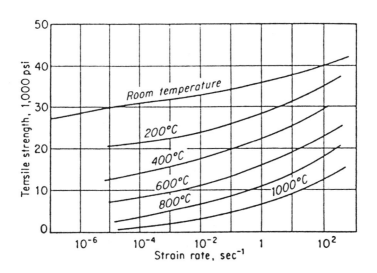

Fig 25. Effects of temperature and strain rate on the strength of copper

For example, dislocations are actually displacements and therefore cannot move faster than the speed of sound. Furthermore, as dislocation velocities approach the speed of sound, cross slip becomes increasingly

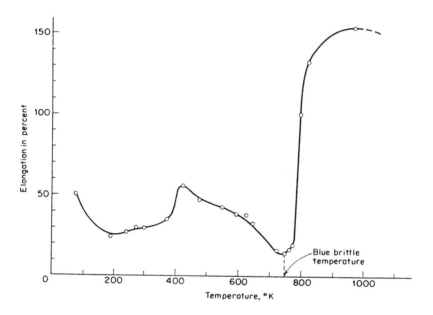

Fig 26. An intermediate-temperature ductility minimum in titanium

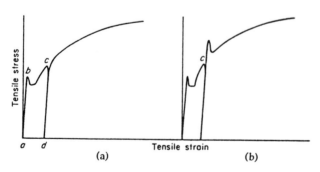

Fig 27. Illustration of strain aging during an interrupted tensile test. (a) Specimen reloaded in a short period of time. (b) Time between loading and unloading is sufficient

difficult and the strain-hardening exponent increases. This increase in the strain-hardening exponent increases the flow stress at any given strain, thus increasing the yield strength of the material. A decrease in ductility and even a transition from ductile to brittle fracture may also be associated with strain-rate-induced increases in yield strength. In many respects, decreasing the temperature is similar to increasing the strain rate. The mobility of dislocations decreases as the temperature decreases, and thus, for most metals and alloys, the strength increases and the ductility decreases as the temperature is lowered. If the reduction in dislocation mobility is sufficient, the ductility may be reduced to the point of brittle fracture. Metals and alloys that show a transition from ductile to brittle when the temperature is lowered should not be used for structural applications at temperatures below this transition temperature.

Dislocation motion is inhibited by interactions between dislocations and alloy or impurity (foreign) atoms. The effects of these interactions are both time and temperature dependent. The interaction acts to increase the yield strength and limit ductility. These processes are most effective when there is sufficient time for foreign atoms to segregate to the dislocation and when dislocation velocities are approximately equal to the diffusion velocity of the foreign atoms. Therefore, at any given

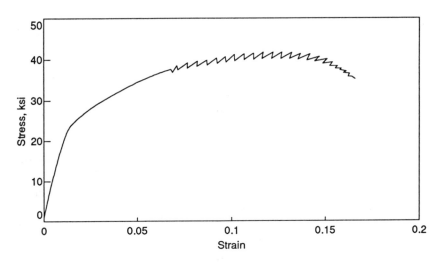

Fig 28. Dynamic strain aging or serrated yielding in an aluminum alloy tested at room temperature

temperature, dislocation–foreign atom interactions will be at a maximum at some intermediate strain rate. At low strain rates, the foreign atoms can diffuse as rapidly as the dislocations move and there is little or no tendency for the deformation process to force a separation of dislocations from their solute atmospheres. At high strain rates, once separation has been effected, there is not sufficient time for the atmosphere to be re-established during the test. Atom movement increases with increasing temperature, thus the strain rates that allow dislocation–foreign atom interactions to occur are temperature dependent. Because these interactions limit ductility, the elongation in a tensile test may show a minimum at intermediate test temperatures where such interactions are most effective (Fig 26).

The effects of time-dependent dislocation foreign atom interactions on the stress-strain curves of metals and alloys are termed "strain aging" and "dynamic strain aging." Strain aging is generally apparent when a tensile test, of a material that exhibits a sharp yield point, is interrupted. If the test specimen is unloaded after being strained past the yield point, through the Lüders strain region and into the strain-hardening portion of the stress-strain curve, either of two behaviors may be observed when the tensile test is resumed (Fig 27). If the specimen is reloaded in a short period of time, the elastic portion of the reloading curve (line d-c in Fig 27a) is parallel to the original elastic loading curve (line a-b in Fig 27a) and plastic deformation resumes at the stress level (level c) that was reached just before the test was interrupted.

However, if the time between unloading and reloading is sufficient for segregation of foreign atoms to the dislocations, the yield point reappears (Fig 27b) and plastic strain is not reinitiated when the unloading stress level (point c) is reached. This reappearance of the yield point is strain aging, and the strength of the strain-aging peak is dependent on both time and temperature because solute-atom diffusion and segregation to dislocations are required for the peak to develop. If tensile strain rates are in a range where solute segregation can occur during the test, dynamic strain aging is observed. Segregation pins the previously mobile dislocations and raises the flow stress, and when the new, higher flow stress is reached the dislocations are separated from the solute atmospheres and the flow stress decreases. This alternate increase and decrease in flow stress causes the stress-strain curve to be serrated (Fig 28).

Serrated flow is common in mild steels, in some titanium and aluminum alloys, and in other metals that contain mobile, alloy or impurity elements. This effect was initially studied in detail by Portevin and LeChatelier and is frequently called the Portevin-LeChatelier effect. Processing conditions must be selected to avoid strain-aging effects. This selection necessarily involves the control of processing strain rates and temperatures.

Special Tests

The tensile test provides basic information concerning the responses of metals and alloys to mechanical loadings. Test temperatures and strain rates (or loading rates) generally are controlled because of the effects of these variables on the metallurgical response of the specimen. The tensile test typically measures strength and ductility. These parameters are frequently sensitive to specimen configuration, test environment, and the manner in which the test is conducted. Special tensile tests have been developed to measure the effects of test/specimen conditions on the strengths and ductilities of metals and alloys. These tests include the notch tensile test and the low-strain-rate tensile test.

Metals and alloys in engineering applications frequently are required to withstand multiaxial loadings and high stress concentrations owing to component configuration. A standard tensile test measures material performance in smooth bar specimens exposed to uniaxial loads. This difference between service and test specimens may reduce the ability of the standard tensile test to predict material response under

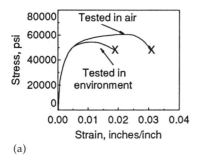

(a)

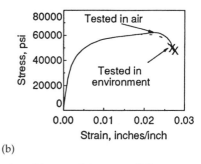

(b)

Fig 29. Typical CERT and SSRT results showing (a) material susceptibility to environmental degradation and (b) material compatibility with the environment

anticipated service conditions. Furthermore the reductions in ductility generally induced by multiaxial loadings and stress concentrations may not be apparent in the test results. The notched tensile test therefore was developed to minimize this weakness in the standard tensile test and to investigate the behavior of materials in the presence of flaws, notches, and stress concentrations.

The notched tensile specimen generally contains a 60° notch that has a root radius of less than 0.025 mm (0.001 in.). The stress state just below the notch tip approaches triaxial tension, and for ductile metals this stress state generally increases the yield strength and decreases the ductility. This increase in yield strength results from the effect of stress state on dislocation dynamics. Shear stresses are required for dislocation motion. Pure triaxial loads do no produce any shear stress; thus, dislocation motion at the notch tip is restricted and the yield strength

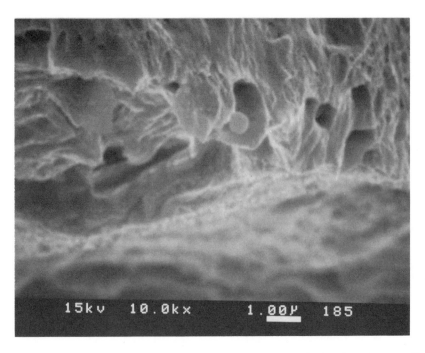

Fig 30. Photomicrograph illustrating fracture initiation at particles. Particle is small sphere near the center of the micrograph

is increased. This restriction in dislocation motion also reduces the ductility of the notched specimen. For low-ductility metals, the notch-induced reduction in ductility may be so severe that failure takes place before the 0.2% offset yield strength is reached.

The sensitivity of metals and alloys to notch effects is termed the "notch sensitivity." This sensitivity is quantified through the ratio of notch strength to smooth bar tensile strength. Metals and alloys that are notch sensitive have ratios less than one. Smooth bar tensile data for these materials are not satisfactory predictors of material behavior under service conditions. Tough, ductile metals and alloys frequently are notch-strengthened and have notch sensitivity ratios greater than one, thus the standard tensile test is a conservative predictor of performance for these materials.

Test environments also may have adverse effects on the tensile behavior of metals and alloys. The characterization of environmental

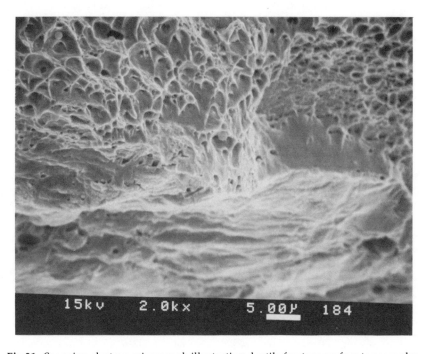

Fig 31. Scanning electron micrograph illustrating ductile fracture surface topography. This fracture topography is identified as microvoid coalescence

effects on material response may be accomplished by conducting the tensile test in the environment of interest. Because the severity of environmental attack generally increases with increasing time, tensile tests designed to determine environmental effects frequently are conducted at very low strain rates. The low strain rate increases the test time and maximizes exposure to the test environment. This type of testing is termed either "slow-strain-rate testing" (SSRT) or "constant-extension-rate testing" (CERT). Exposure to the aggressive environment may reduce the strength and/or ductility of the test specimen. These reductions may be accompanied by the onset of surface cracking and/or a change in the fracture mode. A CERT or SSRT study that shows detrimental effects on the tensile behavior will establish that the test material is susceptible to environmental degradation (Fig 29a).

This susceptibility may cause concern over the utilization of the material in that environment. Conversely, the test may show that the tensile behavior of the material is not influenced by the environment and is therefore suitable for service in that environment (Fig 29b). CERT and SSRT may be used to screen materials for potential service exposures and/or investigate the effects of anticipated operational changes on the materials used in process systems. In either event, the intent is to avoid materials utilization under conditions that may degrade the strength and ductility and cause premature fracture. In addition to the tensile data *per se*, evidence of adverse environmental effects may also

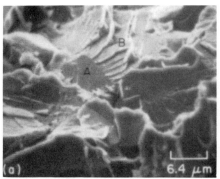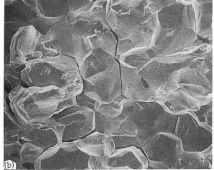

Fig 32. Scanning electron micrographs illustrating transgranular and intergranular fracture topographies. (a) Transgranular cleavagelike fracture topography. Direction of crack propagation is from grain A through grain B. (b) Intergranular fracture topography

be found through examination of the fracture morphologies of CERT and SSRT test specimens.

Fracture Characterization

Tensile fracture of ductile metals and alloys generally initiates internally in the necked portion of the tensile bar. Particles such as inclusions, dispersed second phases, and/or precipitates may serve as the nucleation sites. The fracture process begins by the development of small holes, or microvoids, at the particle-matrix interface (Fig 30).

Continued deformation enlarges the microvoids until, at some point in the testing process, the microvoids contact each other and coalesce. This process is termed "microvoid coalescence" and gives rise to the dimpled fracture surface topography characteristic of ductile failure processes (Fig 31).

The surface topography of a brittle fracture differs significantly from that of microvoid coalescence. Brittle fracture generally initiates at imperfections on the external surface of the material and propagates either by transgranular cleavagelike processes or by separation along grain boundaries. The resultant surface topography is either faceted, perhaps with the riverlike patterns typical of cleavage (Fig 32a), or intergranular, producing a "rock candy"–like appearance (Fig 32b). The test material may be inherently brittle (such as chromium or tungsten), or brittleness may be introduced by heat treatment, lowering the test temperature, the presence of an aggressive environment, and/or the presence of a sharp notch on the test specimen.

The temperature, strain rate, test environment, and other conditions, including specimen surface finish for a tensile test, are generally well established. An understanding of the effects of such test parameters on the fracture characteristics of the test specimen can be very useful in the determination of the susceptibility of metals and alloys to degradation fabrication and during service. Typically, any heat treatment or test condition that causes the fracture process to change from microvoid coalescence to a more brittle fracture mode reduces the ductility and toughness of the material and may promote premature fracture under selected service conditions. Because the fracture process is very sensitive to both the metallurgical condition of the specimen and the conditions of the tensile test, characterization of the fracture surface is an important component of many tensile-test programs.

Summary

The mechanical properties of metals and alloys are frequently evaluated through tensile testing. The test technique is well standardized and can be conducted relatively inexpensively with a minimum of equipment. Many materials utilized in structural applications are required to have tensile properties that meet specific codes and standards. These requirements are generally minimum strength and ductility specifications. Because of this, information available from a tensile test is frequently under utilized. A rather straightforward investigation of many of the metallurgical interactions that influence the results of a tensile test can significantly improve the usefulness of test data. Investigation of these interactions, and correlation with metallurgical/material/service variables such as heat treatment, surface finish, test environment, stress state, and anticipated thermomechanical exposures, can lead to significant improvements in both the efficiency and the quality of materials utilization in engineering service.

5

Tensile Testing of Plastics

S. Turner, Queen Mary and Westfield College,
University of London

Tensile testing embraces various procedures by which modulus, strength, and ductility can be assessed. Tests specifically designed to measure phenomena as varied as creep, stress relaxation, stress rupture, fatigue, and impact resistance can all be classified as tensile tests provided that the stress system is predominantly tensile, but by common usage the term "tensile test" is usually taken to mean a test in which a specimen is extended uniaxially at a uniform rate. Ideally, the specimen should be slender, of constant cross section over a substantial gage length, and free to contract laterally as it extends; a tensile stress then develops over transverse plane sections lying within the gage region, and the specimen extends longitudinally and contracts laterally. A procedure was initially developed for tests on metals but was subsequently adopted and adapted for tests on rubbers, fibers, and plastics. In the case of plastics, their viscoelastic nature and the probable anisotropy of their end products (including test specimens) are factors that strongly influence both the conduct of the tests and the interpretation of the results.

Practical tensile testing often conforms to one or another of several standard methods or to a code of practice, with variants dictated by local circumstances. Most of the stipulations set out in the standardized practices embody the collective wisdom of earlier tensile-test practitioners and fall into four distinct groupings:

1. Stipulations relating to the specimen-machine system

2. Stipulations relating to the derivation of excitation-response relationships from the raw data

3. Stipulations relating to the precision of the data

4. Stipulations relating to the physical interpretation of the data.

The stipulations in the first group are the primary ones, because, unless the specimen-machine system functions properly, no worthwhile data can be generated. The stipulations in the other three groups are supplementary but are nevertheless essential in that they enable the outcome of the machine-specimen interaction to be translated progressively into mechanical-properties data for the specimen under investigation.

Viscoelasticity and anisotropy cast their influences over all these groups. Viscoelasticity influences the excitation-response relationships, complicates the analysis of data, and affects some practical aspects of the test. Anisotropy does the same things, but also introduces an uncertainty about the utility of any specific datum because it varies from point to point in a specimen, and from specimen to specimen in a sample, depending on the processing conditions and other factors. These variations can be large, and therefore questions arise as to how such materials should be evaluated and whether or not results from tests on a particular specimen can ever be definitive. If a test has been properly executed, the properties data should be precise, but they may be precise without being accurate and may be accurate without being definitive.

In one particular respect, tensile testing suffers from a fundamental and inescapable deficiency that is common to many types of mechanical tests: the experimenter has no option but to measure force and deformation, whereas the physical characteristics of the specimen and the material should be expressed in terms of stress and strain. The translations of force into stress and deformation into strain are sources of errors and uncertainties, so much so that the transformed results may bear little relation to the strict truth, although this does not render them useless. Note No. 2 of ASTM D 638, "Standard Test Method for Tensile Properties of Plastics," states, appropos of other factors but appropriate nevertheless, that "This test method is not intended to cover precise physical procedures.... Special additional tests should be used where more precise physical data are required."

Fundamental Factors that Affect Data from Tensile Tests

Viscoelasticity

Plastics are viscoelastic—that is, the relationships between the stress state and the strain state are functions also of time. *Linear* viscoelasticity, the simplest case, is represented by the relationship

$$\sum_{n=0}^{\infty} a_n \frac{\partial^n \sigma}{\partial t^n} = \sum_{m=0}^{\infty} b_m \frac{\partial^m \varepsilon}{\partial t^m}$$

where σ is stress, ε is strain, and t is time, and a and b are characterizing coefficients. When most of the coefficients are set to zero, the equation describes simple behavior. If only a_0 and b_0 differ from zero, the equation represents linear elastic behavior, and if only a_0 or b_1 differs from zero, it represents Newtonian viscosity, but as other coefficients differ from zero the differential terms progressively enter the equation and the relationships between stress and strain then become time-dependent. In simple cases, the viscoelasticity can be visualized as the mechanical behavior of assemblies of Hookean springs and Newtonian dashpots (which are representable by the same equation), the two simplest assemblies being a series combination and a parallel combination of one spring and one dashpot. The former, known as a Maxwell element, is used primarily to represent or demonstrate the time-dependence of the stress that arises when a strain is applied suddenly, and the latter, known as a Voigt element, demonstrates the time-dependence of the strain that develops when a stress is applied suddenly (see Fig 1).

Due allowance must be made for viscoelasticity during both the practical execution of the test and the interpretation of the results, because the ramifications of viscoelasticity extend over virtually all the mechanical behavior. Thus, for example, after the specimen has been

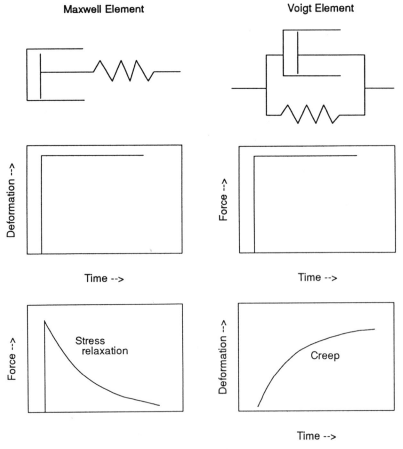

Fig 1. Visualizations of simple viscoelastic systems

mounted in the grips, the clamping stresses may relax to the point where it is not held securely. There are several such specimen-machine interactions, but appropriate practical measures alleviate their consequences, and serious malfunctions generally can be avoided. In contrast, possibilities of misinterpretation of the results are not so easily circumvented, because viscoelasticity is an inescapable feature of almost every response curve. In general, the response of a viscoelastic body to an applied stress or strain is a function of the stress history or the strain history. Therefore, the moduli, which are defined in various ways depending on the time-form of the excitation, are functions of elapsed time and/or frequency (see Fig 1). Furthermore, plastics are *nonlinearly* viscoelastic—that is, at constant time the relationship between stress and strain is nonlinear. The relaxation modulus, which is derived from an experiment in which a strain supposedly is applied instantaneously and held constant thereafter, is a function of the strain magnitude as well as of the elapsed time; similarly, the creep compliance is a function of the stress magnitude and the elapsed time. These two procedures are ideal in that they enable nonlinearity and time-dependence to be separated experimentally, but the apparently simple procedure of conventional tensile testing is not simple; the force or the stress that develops in the course of the test is governed by both the changes in strain and the passage of time.

A single tensile test provides merely one section across a relationship that for plastics is a complex one between stress, strain, and strain rate, and it follows that inferences drawn from that single curve are correspondingly limited in their scope. For instance, such a curve contains no direct indication of load-bearing capability under loads sustained over any period greater than the duration of that particular tensile test. Tensile-testing practice accommodates this and related deficiencies pragmatically by regarding deformation rate as a critical variable. A comprehensive evaluation entails the use of several rates, which should range over several decades, although this raises certain practical issues. Very low rates may be prohibited on the grounds of uneconomical deployment of expensive apparatus, and very high rates pose technical demands on machine power and sensor response that may be resolved more effectively by use of impact tests.

The viscoelasticity, in combination with certain features of the test system itself, influences the choice of data for subsequent conversion into property values. Thus, the modulus, which is a multivalue property if the material is viscoelastic, must be qualified by specification of the current stress (or strain) and the stress (or strain) history up to a specific point in time. For ramp excitations—i.e., the constant deformation-rate conditions of a tensile test—modulus can be defined as the slope of either the tangent at, or the secant to, any desired point on a stress-strain curve. As such, each single datum is one point only in a viscoelastic function; it has no special merit, although, of the various options, the tangent at the origin is possibly the best in theory because the strain-dependence should be negligible there. However, mechanical inertias in the testing machine and finite response times of the sensors combine with the viscoelasticity to distort the observed force-deformation relationship. They reduce the initial slope, obscure the origin, and

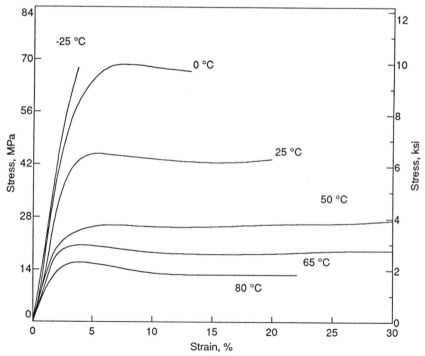

Fig 2. Influence of temperature on the nature of the stress-strain relationship. Strain rate has a similar effect, with increasing rate being equivalent to decreasing temperature. Source: *Engineered Materials Handbook*, Vol 2, ASM International, 1988, p 434

obscure or distort abrupt changes in slope that may signify structural changes in the deforming specimen, thereby detracting from the usefulness of the test and introducing the potential for errors in the measurements.

Strength is also a multivalue property, the viscoelasticity intruding both directly, as a time-dependence (rate-dependence) or the equivalent temperature-dependence, and indirectly, as a factor influencing the nature of the failure or fracture, through the sensitivity to strain rate and temperature of the ductile-brittle transition. This transition is usually a gradual one, with the ductility decreasing progressively as the deformation rate is increased or as the temperature is lowered. The practicalities of the evaluation of tensile properties are such that temperature usually is varied in preference to extension rate; Fig 2 shows typical results from which it may be inferred that the shapes of the stress-strain curves of plastic materials are not uniquely characteristic, and it follows also that uncertainties can arise over the point at which a characterizing datum such as a strength or a yield strain should be extracted from the response curve.

In summary, the viscoelastic nature of plastics entails specific precautions concerning some practical aspects of the test and the analysis of the results. In the first category, mounting of the specimen in the grips and mounting of strain sensors on the specimen require special attention. In the second category, the response curve must be recognized as offering only a limited insight into the mechanical behavior of the sample under investigation, and the data must be used with appropriate caution. See also Fig 3.

Anisotropy in Plastic Specimens

Test specimens, whether directly molded or cut from larger pieces, are often anisotropic—partly because plastics are viscoelastic in their molten state and very viscous, so that the shaping processes cause molecular alignments, and partly because ordered structural entities may develop during the cooling stage.

The property values derivable from such specimens often differ from what might be expected on the basis of isotropic idealizations, and, because of their limited range, the data usually generated are not definitive in that they do not adequately quantify the tensor array of modulus or strength and do not show how that array varies with processing conditions, flow geometry, and specimen geometry. Some of

Tensile Testing

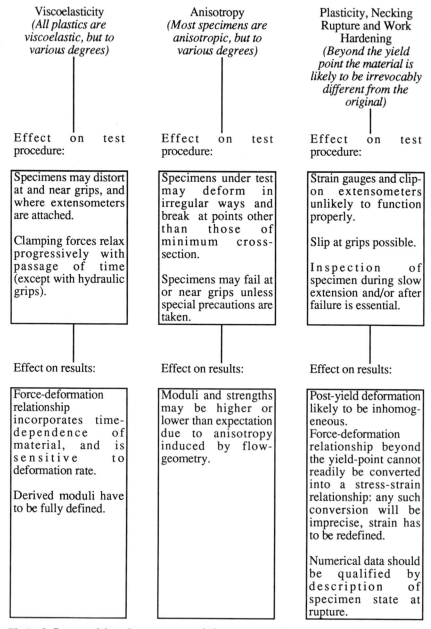

Viscoelasticity (All plastics are viscoelastic, but to various degrees)	Anisotropy (Most specimens are anisotropic, but to various degrees)	Plasticity, Necking Rupture and Work Hardening (Beyond the yield point the material is likely to be irrevocably different from the original)
Effect on test procedure:	**Effect on test procedure:**	**Effect on test procedure:**
Specimens may distort at and near grips, and where extensometers are attached. Clamping forces relax progressively with passage of time (except with hydraulic grips).	Specimens under test may deform in irregular ways and break at points other than those of minimum cross-section. Specimens may fail at or near grips unless special precautions are taken.	Strain gauges and clip-on extensometers unlikely to function properly. Slip at grips possible. Inspection of specimen during slow extension and/or after failure is essential.
Effect on results:	**Effect on results:**	**Effect on results:**
Force-deformation relationship incorporates time-dependence of material, and is sensitive to deformation rate. Derived moduli have to be fully defined.	Moduli and strengths may be higher or lower than expectation due to anisotropy induced by flow-geometry.	Post-yield deformation likely to be inhomogeneous. Force-deformation relationship beyond the yield-point cannot readily be converted into a stress-strain relationship: any such conversion will be imprecise, strain has to be redefined. Numerical data should be qualified by description of specimen state at rupture.

Fig 3. Influence of the inherent nature of plastics on tensile-testing practice

the ramifications have been troublesome in evaluation programs in the past, because certain consequential results have seemed to be anomalous. Two situations are particularly important: one relates to the position of the failure site, and the other relates to the strength of notched specimens.

The first situation involves tensile specimens of dumbbell or similar shape, which often are injection molded through an endgate. The pattern of molecular and fiber orientation is then predominantly longitudinal in the outer layers of the parallel-sided section but is more complex in the core and at the ends of the specimen. At the end remote from the gate, the larger cross section causes diverging flow during the molding operation and therefore some lateral molecular orientation, which may lower the longitudinal strength locally to such a level that the specimen breaks there rather than at the smaller cross section in the gage region.

The second situation involves notched specimens. A molded notch may not affect strength to the same degree, or even in the same sense, that would be inferred from stress-concentration theory, because the local flow geometry near the crack tip may enhance the strength and thereby mitigate the effect of the stress concentration. On the other hand, the flow geometry may reduce the strength in the critical direction. A machined notch also interacts with the flow geometry in that the geometrical details govern where the tip lies in relation to the orientation pattern. Results are likely to be less ambiguous than those for molded notches but still at quantitative variance with predictions based on concepts of stress concentration or stress-field intensity.

A secondary consequence, but one of great practical importance, is that the essentially simple functional operation of the test machine is compromised, particularly in relation to the specimen-machine interaction. The force is transmitted to the specimen mainly by means of shear stresses at or near the grips, and the specimen is required to extend with lateral contraction but no extraneous distortion. However, a predominantly axial molecular orientation or fiber alignment confers a relatively high tensile strength but a relatively low shear strength along the longitudinal direction, with the result that shear failure near the grips may ensue before tensile failure occurs in the gage region. Modified grips, reinforcing plates attached to the ends of specimens, and changed specimen profiles can all reduce the risk of malfunction, but such steps may be detrimental in other respects. If the predominant orientation lies at some angle to the tensile axis, the specimen will distort into a sigmoid, the exact form of which will depend on whether or not the clamped ends are free to rotate; in either case, the observed force and extension will not convert into correct values of tensile modulus or tensile strength. In general, these effects are far more pronounced in specimens of continuous-fiber plastic-matrix composites than in simple plastic specimens (including those containing short fibers); but even if there is no gross malfunction in tests on plastics, there is a high probability of mildly erroneous data being generated.

The influences of flow geometry and flow irregularities on derived property values are pervasive and can distort an investigator's perception of properties, trends, etc. Corrective action to avoid misconceptions entails expansion of the evaluation programs to cover samples with different flow geometries and, in some instances, modified test configurations—e.g., different specimen profiles. The choice of samples and specimens is a complex issue that has never been resolved adequately. Specimens machined from various judiciously chosen positions in larger items are possibly a wiser choice than the widely used injection-molded endgated bars. The latter are popular because they are economical in the use of material and manpower, but the predominantly axial molecular orientation of thin moldings confers higher tensile moduli and strengths than those exhibited by most end products. The pattern of orientation varies with the thickness of the bar; axial orientation arises mainly in the outer layers, and hence, as the thickness increases, the measured values of tensile modulus and strength decrease.

In summary, anisotropy can cause extraneous distortions in specimens under test, failure at or near the grips, unsuspected errors in data, and odd trends with respect to notch geometry, specimen profile, etc. (see also Fig 3). In many instances, the evaluation program should be expanded, possibly with modified test procedures.

Plasticity, Necking Rupture, and Work Hardening

There is much experimental evidence, from creep studies and from tensile tests themselves, that with increasing strain the deformation processes become progressively dominated by molecular mechanisms that either are irreversible or are reversible but have very protracted recovery times. The over-all character of the deformation processes becomes "viscous" rather than "elastic," and the specimen then either extends uniformly or yields by means of a necking mechanism approximately in conformance with plasticity theory. Figure 4 gives a schematic impression of likely yielding and post-yield behavior. A material that has yielded is usually radically different in nature from what it was prior to yielding. The difference may be merely a reordered molecular state, but it also may be the presence of larger-scale discontinuities such as voids, crazes, or interphase cracks, all of which have various and different implications for the service performance of end products.

The yield stress, defined by some identifiable feature on the force-deformation curve, depends on the deformation rate, as does the probability that failure will occur before a neck is established. The higher the

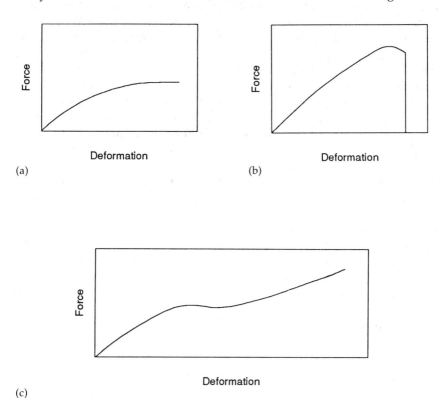

Fig 4. Yielding and post-yield tensile behavior: (a) uniform extension; (b) yielding followed by necking rupture; (c) yielding followed by "cold drawing" and work hardening

deformation rate, the higher the yield stress and the greater the chance that brittle or pseudobrittle failure will intervene. There are two principal reasons for the latter relationship. The temperature and the anisotropy may be such that the ductile-brittle transition is traversed as the deformation rate is increased, or the neck may form but fail to stabilize because of the particular microstructure of the polymer or composition of the plastic. The molecular architecture, the molecular weight, and the degree of branching all affect the propensity of the molecules to align in the neck and the consequential strength there. Similarly, the development of macroscopic discontinuities—e.g., microvoids, phase separations, and crazes—may be detrimental, although not necessarily, because the ligaments may be strengthened by favorably oriented molecules. Another factor is the local temperature, which will rise if the heat generated by virtue of the inherent loss processes exceeds what can be lost to the environment and which may reach a critical point at which the yield stress has fallen to such a level that the neck cannot support the prevailing force. If the neck stabilizes satisfactorily it will travel along the parallel-sided section of the specimen either at an approximately constant force or with a progressively increasing force if the molecular assembly is such that further orientation can occur.

The various features of time-dependent plasticity, necking rupture, inhomogeneous deformation, and work hardening affect the practical execution of tests in that a high extensibility imposes particular requirements on the grips and the deformation sensors, but, more importantly, these features affect the ways in which the derived data should be presented and interpreted (see Fig 3). Thus, a yield stress identified by some features on the force-deformation curve should not be regarded as unambiguously definitive, because there is a zone in which the material is neither wholly viscoelastic nor wholly plastic and, additionally, the material in the neck is not necessarily a continuum. At a more mundane level, if a specimen has necked, the stress and the strain at failure are not readily calculable from the force and deformation data.

Stipulations in Standardized Tensile Testing

The Specimen-Machine System

The superficially simple nature of the tensile test conceals a demanding mechanical requirement. The specimen must be extended uniformly at any one of several prescribed rates, which, when translated into a design specification, entails:

1. Adequate power in a testing machine to ensure that the stiffest specimens can be extended at the designated rates

2. Alignment of the line of action with the axis of symmetry of the specimen, to minimize the variation of stress across the specimen cross section

3. Secure and balanced clamping of the specimen to ensure that it neither slips in the grips nor suffers extraneous forces

4. High-quality specimens of the correct size and profile for the intended purpose and with a fine surface finish

These four design features are interconnected to some degree and are all influenced by the viscoelastic nature of the specimens.

The provision of adequate power poses no direct problem, but there may be secondary difficulties in that a powerful machine is likely to be massive and to have inertias and frictions in the actuator and the likages that are troublesome when the active forces are small—i.e., at low specimen strain or when the specimen has a low modulus or a low strength. The issue is whether a single machine is suitable for testing all classes of plastics at all conceivable strain rates and over the entire strain range to failure. If there is a range of machines at the investigator's disposal, the choice should be governed by the character of the specimen and should be such that the specimen is matched to the machine. The specimen should never dominate the machine, because in such an event the signals being extracted from the test would reflect a complex combination of machine and specimen characteristics. On the other hand, if the machine is excessively dominant, it may impose inadvertent and undesirable constraints on the specimen.

Accurate alignment of the specimen in the machine is not easily achieved, because the machine, the specimen, and the clamping of the one to the other are all prone to asymmetries that can cause misalignment. There are various design choices ranging from sufficient degrees of freedom to allow a misaligned specimen to settle into an aligned position as it begins to extend, at one extreme, to total constraint at the other. The former method relies on the specimen being sufficiently stiff to be essentially unaffected by the adjustment forces, which is unlikely to be the case for a plastic material. Similarly, however, the friction inherent in a fully constrained system may constitute a large error in the measured force.

Machine factors are largely outside the control of a user, but, to varying degrees, specimen-preparation procedures, choice of grips, and operational checks, all of which affect and/or control the axiality of the alignment, are discretionary. Specimens must be symmetrical about their longitudinal axes. One machined from a larger item can be very accurately symmetrical. A directly molded specimen can be similarly accurate, but inappropriate molding conditions or a badly designed mold can produce distorted specimens. Specimens molded from novel or newly developed materials, for which the processing conditions may not have been optimized, are prone to such distortion, but force of circumstance may dictate the data generated from such specimens must be used, despite the imperfections, as a basis for judgments crucial to the further progression of a research or development program. When this is the case, the judgments should be suitably circumspect.

Even if the specimen is satisfactorily symmetrical, it may be clamped unsymmetrically unless special precautions are taken to position it properly in the grips. Use of a hole in each specimen end and corresponding pins in the grips is the simplest solution, and has proved very satisfactory for tensile creep tests. The holes also facilitate the machining operation by defining the axis of symmetry. Ideally, the force should be transmitted to the specimen through the pins rather than through the faces of the grips, but this imposes special requirements on the specimen geometry to limit the chance of shear failure at the pins (see the subsection on anisotropy in plastic specimens), and the less ideal conventional clamping, ostensibly acting across the entire width of the specimen, is commonly preferred.

Misalignment is relatively unimportant if the strength of a ductile material is being measured, because limited plastic deformation suffices to correct the fault and the test progresses unimpaired thereafter. On the other hand, misalignment is a source of error if the strength of a brittle material or the modulus of any type of material is being measured, because the misalignment causes the specimen to bend or unbend, as the case may be, as it is extended in the test. The stress is then nonuniform over the cross section, and one face of the specimen bears a stress higher than the average stress; the measured strength is then likely to be an underestimate of the true strength. The error in the modulus measurement may be positive or negative, depending on the positioning of the strain sensor, and can even be eliminated if the strain on each face of the specimen is measured.

To some degree, there is a conflict of objectives in the design and operation of the grips. Secure clamping is desirable so that the specimen does not slip relative to the grips, or entirely out of the grips, during a test, but it simultaneously prevents self-aligning movement and thereby preserves any initial misalignment. On balance, total constraint is the preferred option. In this case, hydraulic grips are probably the most satisfactory because they exert a pressure that is uniform over the entire face and that remains constant as the specimen extends and correspondingly thins. Simple mechanical grips may have to be overtightened initially, and consequently the specimen may be severely distorted. Such distortion can be reduced or eliminated by the use of reinforcing tabs on the ends of the specimens, but this is a tedious measure that is not widely used for tests on plastics.

The specimen-machine system cannot be expected to operate satisfactorily, however well designed it may be, unless the quality of the specimen is commensurate with the expectations. Methods of specimen production include direct molding, cutting from larger stock with an appropriately shaped guillotine, and machining with a router or milling cutter. Certain procedures must be followed with each method if the symmetry required for axial stressing is to be attained: the cooling systems of molding cavities should be so designed that any residual strains are in equilibrium, specimens being machined should be supported so that they do not distort under the machining forces, etc. The surface finish is also important, because imperfections may act as stress concentrators and cause the specimen to fail prematurely. Unsuitable molding conditions can produce surface textures and imperfections ranging from the visually obvious to the submicroscopic. Guillotine cutters are fast in operation but often produce specimens with poor edge faces. In general, milling cutters and routers produce better surface finishes than guillotines, but this depends on the cutting speed, which should be high but not so high that generated heat softens or melts the surface.

Tensile Testing

The various elements of the specimen-machine interaction that affect the over-all operation efficiency in the tensile testing of plastics are summarized in Fig 5.

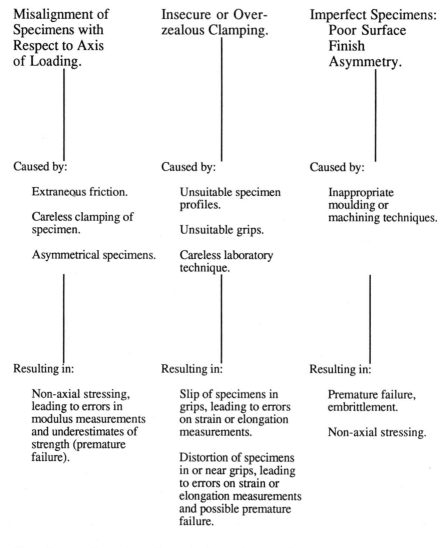

Misalignment of Specimens with Respect to Axis of Loading.	Insecure or Over-zealous Clamping.	Imperfect Specimens: Poor Surface Finish Asymmetry.
Caused by:	**Caused by:**	**Caused by:**
Extraneous friction. Careless clamping of specimen. Asymmetrical specimens.	Unsuitable specimen profiles. Unsuitable grips. Careless laboratory technique.	Inappropriate moulding or machining techniques.
Resulting in:	**Resulting in:**	**Resulting in:**
Non-axial stressing, leading to errors in modulus measurements and underestimates of strength (premature failure).	Slip of specimens in grips, leading to errors on strain or elongation measurements. Distortion of specimens in or near grips, leading to errors on strain or elongation measurements and possible premature failure.	Premature failure, embrittlement. Non-axial stressing.

Fig 5. Sources of experimental error in the specimen-machine system

120

Derivation of Excitation-Response Relationships

Many investigators require only a single datum from a tensile test and naturally tend to regard the derivation procedure as a simple operation, which it may be when the testing machine is set up with a single objective in mind. The over-all operation, however, is a more complex matter, the single datum being only a small element in the total response of the specimen. The excitation-response relationship provides numerical values of various mechanical properties—e.g., modulus and yield strength; also, in its entirety it gives an over-all impression of "tensile characteristics" although, as was pointed out in the subsection on viscoelasticity, each curve provides only one section across a complex relationshipbetween stress, strain, and strain rate. The particular type of excitation used in tensile testing was originally chosen for its mechanical simplicity; it loosely approximates a ramp function of strain versus time, which is not particularly tractable analytically even for a linear viscoelastic body and is even less tractable for a nonlinear one. Thus, because of both practical and theoretical limitations, it is unlikely that the observable response can ever be translated into fundamental quantities at the molecular level—for example, relaxation time spectra.

However, irrespective of the details, information can be obtained from a test only if there are suitable sensors to convert the excitation and response into numerical or analog data. These sensors must have sensitivities and response times that are appropriate for the intended purpose of the test. The sensitivity should be such that the sensor discriminates at, say, 1% of full scale display, and the response time should be such that the fine structure of response is detected even though this generally entails the likelihood that extraneous vibrations in the machine will be incorporated as noise in the signal. The observable quantities are limited to force and deformation, and the former is actually measured as deformation in a transducer.

The force is always measured directly and accurately provided that the machine and the transducer are adequately stiff. The deformation up to the yield point may be measured directly by means of an extensometer attached to the specimen, strain gages bonded to it, or an independent optical device operating without physical contact. These methods entail careful and sometimes expensive subsidiary operations, and, furthermore, only the remote optical devices are practicable beyond the yield point. Consequently, for certain classes of test, they may be dispensed with, the deformation then being measured indirectly as actuator movement, with possible corrections for extraneous effects caused by clamping and the specimen profile.

Strain gages and clip-on extensometers have their respective advantages and disadvantages. The former are more troublesome to mount on the specimen and measure the strain over only a small zone, but, on the other hand, they can be so positioned as to measure strain along whichever direction is of interest. Clip-on gages provide an average strain over a larger span. They are less versatile in relation to strain axis but can measure transverse strains, and therefore the change in volume during a test can be determined by either type of sensor. Such information provides insight into pre-yield mechanisms.

In the case of modulus measurement, the strains involved are small and the over-all deformation is homogeneous; force translates easily into stress with only small errors, and deformation can be measured over a defined gage length. In principle, deformation measurements should be accurate in such situations, but clip-on extensometers may slip if the retaining spring force is small or may indent the specimen if the spring force is large, and bonded strain gages may affect the surface strain that they are intended to measure if the stiffness of the specimen is low. Even so, with minor reservations, the modulus can be measured to a satisfactory precision. Coefficients of variation of about 0.03 are commonplace, and coefficients of 0.02 are attainable.

In the case of strength tests, the over-all precision of the measurements is lower—primarily because the calculation of stress is inevitably an approximation, and secondarily because extraneous defects in the specimen may promote failure or induce brittleness. If the failure is brittle, the calculated strength can be based on the initial cross-sectional area, but this measured quantity may be neither precise nor accurate because of nonaxial loading, defects in the specimen, or variable anisotropy. Coefficients of variation of 0.10 for the interspecimen variability are commonplace, and the values may be a substantial underestimate of the true strength. If the failure is ductile, the estimate of area is likely to be erroneous, and if the deformation is also inhomogeneous, as is common, the calculation of failure stress is further confounded. The nominal yield stress calculated on the basis of the initial cross section is likely to be precise, with a coefficient of variation of about 0.03, but not highly accurate because of the complexity of the associated phenomena. In contrast, the nominal breaking stress of a specimen that extends beyond the yield point is little more than a normalized break-ing force and is physically meaningless.

The deformation or strain at failure is similarly a dubious quantity. It is usually inferred from the movement of the actuator, because strain gages and extensometers normally are not used in tests that are intended to progress to failure of the specimen. With brittle fracture, the error in the inferred deformation is usually large, because extrane-ous deformations at and near the grips constitute a relatively large proportion of the over-all movement of the actuator. This source of error is less influential when the failure is ductile, but the measured deformation usually does not then translate directly into strain. Even so, the commonly quoted extension to fracture is a useful quantity because it relates loosely to the stability of the neck, the propensity of the specimen for subsequent work hardening, and the incidence of defects in the specimen. There are no quantitative rules for underpin-ning of judgments on these matters, and the investigator must assess new results against a background of whichever accrued data are appro-priate. The same is true, to varying degrees, of most of the data relating to failure; they are accommodated within a framework of comprehen-sion that enables useful information to be extracted despite uncertain-ties about the physical credentials of the experimental data. This framework of comprehension is based on the collective experience of many previous investigators, accumulations of data, established corre-lations between test results and service performance, perceptions of quality, and other knowledge. It follows that the reliability of such rationalizations depends heavily on the quality of the database.

The principle sources of error that are encountered in this phase of the testing operation are summarized in Fig 6. In combination, the various sources of error summarized in Fig 3, 5, and 6 often lead to coefficients of variation of 0.10 or higher; at this level, the imprecision is such that ten nominally identical specimens should be tested for the derivation of a property value (most standard specifications stipulate a minimum of five).

Physical Interpretation of Data

The force-determination relationships of specimens are converted by calculation and inference into stress-strain relationships for the constituent material. At low strains, this stress-strain relationship defines various moduli, and, provided that appropriate procedural

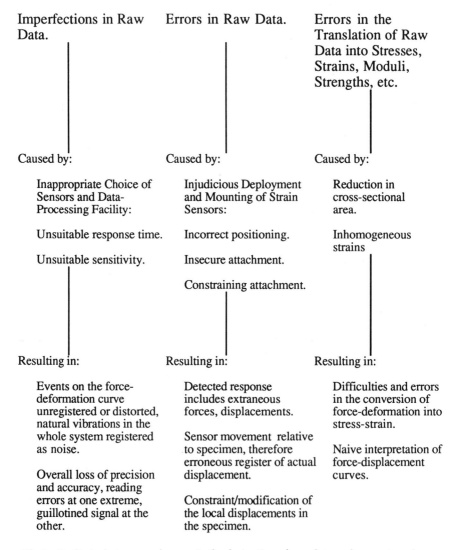

Imperfections in Raw Data.	Errors in Raw Data.	Errors in the Translation of Raw Data into Stresses, Strains, Moduli, Strengths, etc.
Caused by:	Caused by:	Caused by:
Inappropriate Choice of Sensors and Data-Processing Facility:	Injudicious Deployment and Mounting of Strain Sensors:	Reduction in cross-sectional area.
Unsuitable response time.	Incorrect positioning.	Inhomogeneous strains
Unsuitable sensitivity.	Insecure attachment.	
	Constraining attachment.	
Resulting in:	Resulting in:	Resulting in:
Events on the force-deformation curve unregistered or distorted, natural vibrations in the whole system registered as noise.	Detected response includes extraneous forces, displacements.	Difficulties and errors in the conversion of force-deformation into stress-strain.
	Sensor movement relative to specimen, therefore erroneous register of actual displacement.	Naive interpretation of force-displacement curves.
Overall loss of precision and accuracy, reading errors at one extreme, guillotined signal at the other.	Constraint/modification of the local displacements in the specimen.	

Fig 6. Faulty techniques and errors in the derivation of raw data and property values

precautions are taken, the accuracy of the modulus data can be high. If the specimens are brittle, the precision of the measured strength may also be high, but the accuracy is likely to be low because of the deleterious effects of imperfections in the specimens. As the strain increases—beyond, say, 0.02—the conversions become progressively more approximate, and therefore, even though the original test results may have been precise, the final strength data are unlikely to be accurate. Even so, the approximations and oversimplifications entailed in this stage are minor impediments in comparison with those involved in the train of inference leading from the over-all bulk values derived from the test to the local values prevailing at the site of fracture of failure. The theories of fracture mechanics and plasticity, taken in conjunction with a mathematical model of the local situation, provide some conversion rules, and it is possible, therefore, for an investigator to gain an insight into micromechanical behavior from macromechanical data. Some procedures, however, are too cumbersome for routine use, and are also questionable to the extent that some doubt persists about the over-all quality of the data generated by them.

The features on a force-determination curve that are taken as identifying important events such as yielding or the onset of critical crack growth may have been chosen more for their macroscopic convenience than for their physical validity, one practical consequence being the enhancement of precision at the expense of accuracy or realism. The diagram in Fig 7 summarizes the possible ambiguity over the identification of the "yield point" in even the simplest case—i.e., when the force-determination curve passes through a maximum. The possible error in the measured yield stress is likely to be small because of the shape of the force-deflection curve as the yield point is approached; on the other hand, for the same reason, an estimate of the yield strain is likely to be imprecise. Where there is no maximum, the characterizing point may be less easily identified and will almost certainly be associated with different physical manifestations; the derived yield stress may be as prone to error as the derived yield strain. Similarly with brittle failure, the error in the critical stress-field intensity factor may be large because of the shape of the rising flank of the curve and because the selected feature may not mark the critical point; for instance, the dominant peak may denote the over-all collapse of the specimen as a load-bearing structure rather than the point at which the growth of the crack becomes critical.

If an investigator needs to clarify such points or to study the phenomena in greater detail, supplementary tests can be helpful. Photography of the specimen at specific moments or continually throughout the test enables correlations to be established between the features on the force-deformation curve and the physical events in the specimen. The simplest expedient is nothing more than a supplementary tensile

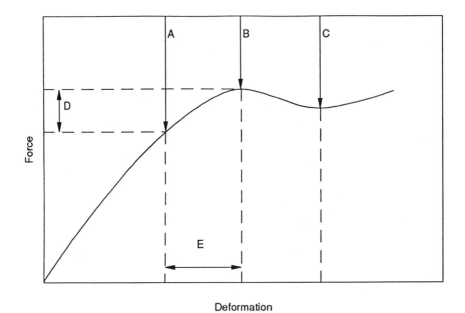

Deformation

A.   Point at which localized yielding may be observed

B.   Point at which resistance to further deformation decreases

C.   Band of uncertainty over yield stress

D.   Band of uncertainty over yield stress

E.   Band of uncertainty over yield strain

Fig 7. Simple force-deformation curve. The maximum force usually is taken as signifying the onset of yielding, but it merely marks the point at which the specimen, as a structure, becomes less resistant to further deformation. Thus, the yield stress and the yield strain are not unambiguously quantifiable.

test at an extension rate sufficiently low for the correlations to be established through visual inspection of the extending specimen; such a test can even be interrupted temporarily to permit a more intense scrutiny, although when an interrupted tensile test is resumed the subsequent force-deformation relationship will differ from that of an uninterrupted test because of viscoelastic relaxation during the static period.

As the extension progresses beyond the yield region, the link between the observed force-deformation relationship and the inferred stress-strain relationship becomes progressively more tenuous. The causes are the aforementioned approximations entailed in the translations of force into stress and deformation into strain, developing inhomogeneities in the specimen and molecular and structural rearrangements in the material. In the post-yield region, the measurable quantities are the ultimate strength, commonly defined as force divided by initial cross-sectional area; the elongation to fracture, derived from the actuator movement; the shape of the curve immediately after necking; and the over-all slope of the curve. These are all characterizing quantities for the force-deformation curve, but it is important that they be regarded as nothing more. These quantities have to be transformed into characterizing quantities for the specimen as an engineering entity, and the reliability of this operation depends on the validity of the mathematical model that is chosen to simulate the mechanical behavior of the specimen. There must be a second transformation, into characterizing data for the material. This is the more difficult of the two, because the flow geometry and processing conditions inherent in the production of specimens impose particular states of molecular order, aggregation, etc., that govern the anisotropy and the levels of the property values. Thus, even though data may be precise and accurate, they may not be representative of the material properties as manifested in the majority of end products, and therefore they may be either unsuitable for some purposes or misleading.

Thermoplastics differ in their sensitivities to flow geometry and processing conditions. High molecular weights, discrete second phases, and large crystal entities tend to worsen the anisotropy, and the consequential ranges of property values can be large—for example, a factor of two for modulus and a factor of three for strength. However, such large ranges normally do not appear as overt variabilities, because the specimen-preparation routines have been standardized and restricted in the interests of reproducibility and operational economy rather than in the interests of practical relevance. Furthermore, the data so generated usually lie near the upper limit of attainable values and are therefore potentially misleading.

The nebulous nature of the post-yield data and the potential variation in all data do not detract unduly from the usefulness of the data, because there are many semiquantitative correlations between the characterizing features and property values on the one hand and certain attributes and properties of end products on the other. For example, even though elongation to fracture varies with the shape of the specimen and cannot be equated accurately with strain, a high value is generally a desirable attribute that is indicative of probable toughness in service items. Intersample differences often can be attributed to specific factors such as molecular weight and the incidence of flaws, contaminants, defects, etc., but results must always be judged in the context of the particular evaluation program and set against an established pattern of data. The over-all success depends on the quality of the infrastructure and the database.

Utilization of Data from Tensile Tests

Materials Evaluation

Tensile tests are multipurpose, the data derived from them being commonly used for purposes ranging from quality control to research. The ubiquitous tables of properties feature modulus, tensile strength, and elongation to fracture derived from tensile tests, but for only one standard deformation rate and one temperature (23 °C, or 73 °F), whereas an emerging body of opinion contends that data for other rates and temperatures should be provided by the data generators. Such steps as the recommendations regarding tensile strength in BS 7008, "Method for the Presentation of Basic Properties of Plastics Part 2. Multi-Point Data," and ISO/DP 11403-1, "Acquisition and Presentation of Multipoint Data Part 1: Mechanical Properties," for example, signify a recognition of the influence of viscoelasticity on tensile properties.

The current minimum evaluation scheme falls far short of what is now being called for formally, and even the latter calls for less than what could be derived from tensile tests, namely:

1. The tensile modulus (tangent and secant) at various strains below the yield point

2. The lateral contraction ratios

3. The yield stress and, in some instances, the yield strain

4. The "load drop" after yielding

5. The slope of force versus deformation after the yield point

6. The ultimate strength (based on initial cross-sectional area)

7. The elongation to fracture.

As discussed in previous sections, these quantities are measurable to different levels of precision, have variously dubious claims to the status of physical properties, and all relate to the specimen rather than to the material from which it has been made. It follows that they should be interpreted with caution. Above all, an evaluator/investigator should bear two points in mind whenever the results/data are being communicated to others:

1. Data at one deformation rate and one temperature may not be adequately representative of the tensile properties and fall short of prospective recommendations on data generation and presentation.

2. Whatever the range of test conditions and whatever the information extracted from the test, the data relate to the specimen; the properties of the sample and of the material must be inferred.

Despite these reservations, the types of data presented in the seven-item list above serve a variety of purposes satisfactorily, although they are also subject to misinterpretation and misuse. Misinterpretation by the investigator can result from:

1. Reliance on a single datum, and failure to make use of the entire force-deformation relationship

2. Failure to impose independent checks on inferences drawn from the data.

Misuse by the investigator and others can result from:

1. Disregard of the possible uniqueness of each sample

2. Insufficient regard for the potentially deleterious effects of unfavorable flow geometries

3. Disregard of the boundaries beyond which particular data are invalid or irrelevant.

Materials Comparisons and Selection

The elementary table of properties on which many comparisons are based features tensile modulus, tensile yield strength, ultimate tensile strength, and ultimate elongation. It is currently criticized for its various shortcomings, but it may owe its simple form to the fact that, for some purposes, many data on each of many properties or pseudoproperties may be confusing rather than enlightening. On the other hand, judgments in some areas require special or selective data, and judgments in other areas require data that extend far beyond the confines of "single-point" data. Thus, the criteria by which a material is chosen in preference to others vary with circumstance, in accordance with often subjective rules. Attempts have been made, and are being made, to automate the operation, which entails a pseudoquantification of the judgment processes, but this latter step is generally a difficult one because the specification for the end product often asks for a combination of property values or characteristics that are mutually exclusive.

One such dilemma arises regularly in the perpetual search for an optimum balance between modulus and ductility, which relate, respectively, to stiffness and toughness in an end product. Practical experience has provided the rough working rule, which also has a basis in theory, that the two properties are reciprocally related, and it follows, therefore, that an acceptable balance at one temperature and deformation rate may not be sustained under different conditions. Currently, the two requisite measurements often are made by independent techniques that use specimens of different shapes, but the tensile test offers the advantage of them being measured on one specimen in one operation.

Decisions about the data formats and logic pathways for materials comparison and selection lie generally outside the scope and influence of the evaluators/investigators, although these workers can nevertheless exert an indirect influence through the tactics and strategies that they adopt for testing and evaluation. It is desirable, in the longer term, that any such steps should be formalized by modifications of existing standard test methods, but this is always a protracted process because of the necessary consultation stage, and as an interim measure limited but useful enhancements of the data can be achieved by strict observance of those strictures of the standards that relate to the qualifying information that describes and specifies the test sample. This suggestion is not likely to recommend itself to people heavily engaged in testing, because the qualifying data can be more voluminous than the actual property data, although there is a growing realization that the latter are virtually useless without the former.

Design Data

The principle underlying design calculations is that the behavior of a structure under a system of forces can be deduced from a formula combining relevant material properties with an appropriate form factor. The property values used should be appropriate for the practical situation to which the design calculation relates—i.e., service temperature, pattern of loading, flow geometry, and other influential factors should all be considered. A distinction is drawn between "design data" and single-point property data, the implication being that the former have a higher status. However, this distinction is an artificial one because even a single datum, such as a modulus or a strength derived from a tensile test, may be used in a design calculation provided that adjustments are made to allow for the differences between the laboratory test conditions and the service/design situation.

At least some of the adjustment factors can be derived from other tensile tests. Thus, anisotropy and other consequences of specific processing conditions and flow geometries can be assessed by tests on appropriately chosen specimens and samples. On the other hand, adjustments that allow for long loading times, intermittent loading, or similar situations must be based on independent creep, creep-rupture, and fatigue tests that are specifically structured to identify and quantify the response of specimens to such loading patterns.

The degree of adjustment varies with the polymer architecture, the composition of the plastic, and the operative factor. If the strength of a standard injection-molded endgated tensile bar is taken as a reference point, an unfavorable flow geometry can reduce the strength to 50% of the reference value, and a long loading period can reduce it to 20% of the reference value, for example. To use unadjusted data in a design for service conditions radically different from those of the test would be to misuse them.

Summary

Tensile testing produces information about the mechanical behavior of specimens subjected to a predominantly tensile stress. The scope and quality of that information depend mainly on the degree of practical finesse that is deployed. The main factors that can affect the outcome of the test program are:

- Sample and specimen selection
- Machine design and function
- Specimen preparation
- Choice and mounting of sensors
- Specimen-machine interaction
- Translation of sensor signals into properties data
- Trains of inference.

However, the over-all test procedure and the strategy depend on the purpose of the test; comprehensive evaluations are expensive, and curtailed evaluations are relatively uninformative.

The over-all balance of the machine-specimen system affects the precision, and to some degree the accuracy, of the raw data. The choices of sample, specimen geometry, specimen position and alignment with respect to the sample, and number of specimens tested affect the precision, accuracy, and fitness-for-purpose of the derived data.

The raw data take the form of a relationship between force and deformation, which can be converted into approximations of a stress-strain relationship and other properties. The raw data and the transformed data relate only to the specific conditions of the test.

The mean value of a measured quantity and the standard deviation as derived from a small subset of nominally identical specimens are approximations of the true mean and standard deviation of a large set of nominally identical specimens.

A tensile test provides data relating to the specimen tested. Tensile-property values derived from one type of specimen drawn from a sample do not fully characterize the tensile properties of the entire sample, and the tensile property values of one sample do not usually suffice to characterize the tensile properties of the constituent material.

Finally, tensile properties alone do not characterize the mechanical behavior of a specimen, sample, or material, although they constitute invaluable indicators.

6

Tensile Testing of Elastomers

R.J. Del Vecchio, Technical Consulting Services

Elastomers comprise a subclass of the larger group of materials, based on very large molecules, called polymers. Various common plastics such as polystyrene and polyethylene, and other materials such as household films and wraps, are polymer-base materials but are not called elastomers because of their limited capacity for reversible stretching. Elastomers must display the ability to stretch and recover that is typical of a rubber band.

A test of the tensile strength of an elastomer can yield readings of several different properties. In some cases these properties are totally independent of each other, and in other cases they are interrelated. At times, some will be of more interest than others, depending on what is being investigated or controlled.

Some nomenclature should be defined. Although the terms "elastomer" (from "elastic polymer") and "rubber" at one time had slightly different meanings, they have become synonymous for all practical purposes. These terms are used to designate the mixture of polymer and other ingredients that makes up a rubber formulation. Each unique formulation is called a "compound," much as a mixture of metals is known as an alloy.

Naturally, the first property of interest determined in a tensile test is the ultimate tensile strength. For elastomers, a class of materials that contain substantial numbers of very different polymers, tensile strength can range from as low as 3.5 MPa (500 psi) to as high as 55.2 MPa (8.0 ksi); however, the great majority of common elastomers tend to fall in the range from 6.9 to 20.7 MPa (1.0 to 3.0 ksi).

The second property noted is ultimate elongation, which is the property that defines elastomeric materials. Any material that can be reversibly elongated to twice its unstressed length falls within the formal ASTM definition of an elastomer. The upper end of the range for rubber compounds is about 800%, and although the lower end is supposed to be 100% (a 100% increase of the unstressed reference dimension), some special compounds that fall slightly below 100% elongation still are accepted as elastomers.

The third characteristic that may be of interest is referred to in the rubber industry as the modulus of the compound, but a specific designation such as 100% modulus or 300% modulus is used. That is due to the fact that the number generated is not an engineering modulus in the normal sense of the term, but rather is the stress required to obtain a given strain. Therefore, the "100% modulus," also referred to as M-100, is simply the stress required to elongate the rubber to twice its reference length.

A final characteristic that can be measured, but that is used less often than the other three, is called "tension set." Often, when a piece of rubber is stretched to final rupture, the recovery in length of the two sections resulting from the break is less than complete. It is possible to measure the total length of the original reference dimension and calculate how much longer the total length of the two separate sections is. This is expressed as a percentage. Some elastomers will exhibit almost total recovery, whereas others may display tension set as high as 10% or more. Tension set may also be measured on specimens stretched to less than breaking elongation.

Idiosyncrasies of Tensile Testing of Elastomers

Because elastomers are enormously different in molecular structure from other materials such as metals, and in fact are complex organic composites of numerous ingredients of very differing characteristics, it is not surprising that they tend to exhibit special effects. It is important to understand what some of these effects are, and how significant they can be.

Very often the processing of the mixture that makes up the elastomer results in some level of orientation of the molecules involved. This structuring of the molecular matrix is commonly referred to as the "grain" of the rubber, and tensile properties usually differ to a detectable degree with and across the grain. This anisotropy may not be significant or even exist in actual elastomeric components, depending on both the specific compound and its processing history. When the grain direction can be determined from knowledge of the processing, tensile testing is done parallel to the grain.

Over 20 different types of polymers can be used as bases for elastomeric compounds, and each type can have a significant number of contrasting subtypes within it. Properties of different polymers can be markedly different: for instance, urethanes seldom have tensile strengths below 20.7 MPa (3.0 ksi) whereas silicones rarely exceed 8.3 MPa (1.2 ksi). Natural rubber is known for high elongation, 500 to 800%, whereas fluoroelastomers typically have elongation values ranging from 100 to 250%.

Literally hundreds of compounding ingredients are available, including major classes such as powders (carbon black, clays, silicas), plasticizers (petroleum-base, vegetable, synthetic), and curatives (reactive chemicals that change the gummy mixture into a firm, stable elastomer). A rubber formulation can contain from four or five ingredients to 20 or more. The number, type, and level of ingredients can be used to change dramatically the properties of the resulting compound, even if the polymer base remains exactly the same.

Tensile Testing

Thus, the same base material—polychloroprene (widely known as neoprene), for example—can be used by the rubber chemist to make compounds as soft as a baby-bottle nipple or as hard as a hockey puck, with tensile strengths ranging from less than 6.9 MPa (1.0 ksi) to more than 20.7 MPa (3.0 ksi) and elongation values from 150 to 600%. Considering the wide varieties of starting polymers and ingredient choices, it is understandable that extremely broad contrasts in properties are found among elastomers.

In addition, tensile properties of elastomers are sensitive to factors involved in specimen preparation. The majority of the time, specimens are cut from molded sheets of rubber. This is done using sharpened dies of a specific dumbbell shape, and the smoothness and sharpness of the die are important. Any nick or tiny tear along the edge of the cut specimen can act as a crack initiator and lead to premature failure of the specimen. Inappropriately low levels of ultimate tensile strength and elongation can be observed in such instances.

Similarly, lack of thoroughness in mixing of the ingredients can lead to poor dispersion, and careless mixing can cause incorporation of small foreign particles in the rubber. Either case will again lead to lower and less precise test results.

Use of specimens other than the standard type called for in the ASTM procedures (see below) is sometimes necessary. Pieces from large moldings can be cut out and ground to reasonable flatness and appropriate thickness, or strips of small tubing can be tested. Correlation between such specimens and standard types is not always precise. Ground specimens do not have the smooth, molded surfaces of laboratory specimens, and therefore it is very likely that cracks will propagate from surface imperfections in the early stages of strain, leasing to tensile rupture at lower elongations. Because the stress-strain curve is terminated at a lower strain, the associated tensile force is automatically lower as well, and thus nonstandard specimens seem to display lower values of elongation and tensile strength than lab specimens of identical material.

Differences in test results between lab specimens and specimens cut from actual parts may also be caused partly by another variable—the level of vulcanization of the elastomer, also called its "state of cure." It is difficult to determine whether or not the state of cure for a lab specimen is truly the same as that for a specimen cut from a large article.

138

Vulcanization, which is the formation of chemical crosslinks between the long chains of the polymer molecules, is usually accomplished through exposure to some level of heat over time. Although different thermal cycles may yield rubber articles that appear and feel the same, their properties can vary appreciably. The various tensile properties will change in different degrees with increasing thermal treatment, so that there is seldom an optimum state of cure in the sense of all of the compound properties reaching their ideal levels simultaneously. For instance, tensile strength may reach a maximum following some particular curing cycle, whereas elongation at that point is well along a steeply decreasing curve.

Thus, the optimum curing cycle for molding of a given compound must be determined through various means too diverse to be explained here, and that curing cycle must then be used consistently for test specimens made of that compound. Otherwise, differences in tensile properties that do not truly relate to any real difference in the formulation will very likely be observed.

At times, a compound will be tested at its normal cure level, and then a second set of samples not only will be molded with the standard curing cycle, but will then undergo an additional phase of high-temperature exposure prior to thermal testing. This thermal aging, usually done in an oven at a combination of temperature and time appropriate to the particular type of elastomer, will result in definite changes in the polymer matrix.

Such changes are reflected in alteration of the tensile-test results. Reduction in elongation is typical, but ultimate tensile strength may increase or decrease. The degree of change of tensile properties resulting from thermal aging is frequently used as an indicator of the compound's ability to withstand aging and/or lower thermal exposure over long time periods. One rule of thumb is that the time required at a given temperature for a compound's tensile strength to drop to about half its original level represents the functional life of the compound at that temperature.

A more subtle effect on standard test results is the effect of time delay between vulcanization and testing of the elastomer. Various complex processes continue to take place in the polymeric matrix for some time after molding is completed, which can affect tensile properties. Therefore, normal procedures call for a minimum delay of 8 h between molding and testing. However, in certain production situations for which such a delay is not tolerable, a correlation could be developed between "warm testing" results—i.e., from tests run within a short time of the sample being vulcanized—and those from standard procedures.

Aside from the types of specimen-preparation effects mentioned above, there are also significant effects from differing test conditions. The great bulk of testing is done at room temperature and a standard rate of elongation, but occasionally special conditions will be called for. For instance, knowledge of tensile strength at some elevated temperature is sometimes desired. Raising or lowering test temperature usually has an inverse effect on tensile strength that can be very substantial, changing it by a factor of two or more.

ASTM Standard D 412

The official standard for tensile testing of elastomers is ASTM D 412. It specifies two principal varieties of specimens: the more commonly used dumbbell-type die cut from a standard test slab 150 by 150 by 20 mm (6 by 6 by 0.8 in.), and actual molded rings of rubber. The second type was standardized for use by the O-ring industry. For both varieties, several possible sizes are permitted, although, again, more tests are run on one of the dumbbell specimens (cut using the Die C shape) than on all other types combined. Straight specimens are also permitted, but their use is discouraged because of a pronounced tendency to break at the grip points, which makes the results less reliable.

The power-driven equipment used for testing is described, including details such as the jaws used to grip the specimen, temperature-controlled test chambers when needed, and the crosshead speed of 500 mm/min (20 in./min). The testing machine must be capable of measuring the applied force within 2%, and a calibration procedure is described. Various other details, such as die-cutting procedures and descriptions of fixtures, are also provided.

The method for determining actual elongation can be visual, mechanical, or optical, but is required to be accurate within 10% increments. In the original visual technique, the machine operator simply held a scale behind or alongside the specimen as it was being stretched and noted the progressive change in the distance between two lines marked on the center length of the dogbone shape. The degree of precision that could be attained using a hand-held ruler behind a piece of rubber being stretched at a rate of over 75 mm/s (3 in./s) was always open to question, with 10% being an optimistic estimate.

More recent technology employs extensometers, which are comprised of pairs of very light grips that are clamped onto the specimen and whose motion is then measured to determine actual material elongation. The newest technology involves optical methods, in which highly contrasting marks on the specimen are tracked by scanning devices, with the material elongation again being determined by the relative changes in the reference marks.

Normal procedure calls for three specimens to be tested from each compound, with the median figure being reported. Provision is also made for use of five specimens on some occasions, with the median again being used.

Techniques for calculating the tensile stress, tensile strength, and elongation are described for the different types of test specimens. The common practice of using the unstressed cross-sectional area for calculation of tensile strength is used for elastomers as it is for many other materials. It is interesting to note that if the actual cross-sectional area at fracture is used to calculate true tensile strength of an elastomer, values that are higher by orders of magnitude are obtained.

In recent years, attention has been given to estimating the precision and reproducibility of the data generated in this type of testing. Interlaboratory test comparisons involving up to ten different facilities have been run, and the later versions of ASTM D 412 contain the information gathered.

Variability of the data for any given compound is to some degree related to that particular formulation. When testing was performed on three different compounds of very divergent types and property levels, the pooled value for repeatability of tensile-strength determinations within labs was about 6%, whereas reproducibility between labs was much less precise, at about 18%. Comparable figures for ultimate elongation were approximately 9% (intralab) and 14% (interlab).

Surprisingly, the same comparisons for M-100 showed much less precision, with intralab variation of almost 20% and interlab variation of over 31%. The theory had been held for some time that, because tensile strength and ultimate elongation are failure properties, and as such are profoundly affected by details of specimen preparation, tensile modulus figures would be more narrowly distributed. Because the data given above clearly do not support such a theory, some other factor must be at work. Possibly it is the lack of precision with which the 100% strain point is observed, but in any case it was important to determine the actual relationship between the precision levels of the different property measurements.

Significance and Use of Tensile-Testing Data

The meaning of tensile strength of elastomers must not be confused with the meaning of tensile strength of other materials such as metals. Whereas tensile strength of a metal may be validly and directly used for a variety of design purposes, this is not true for elastomers. As stated early in ASTM D 412, "Tensile properties may or may not be directly related to the end use performance of the product because of the wide range of performance requirements in actual use." In fact, it is very seldom if ever that a given high level of tensile strength of a compound can be used as evidence that the compound is fit for some particular application.

It is important to note that the tensile properties of elastomers are determined by a single application of progressive strain to a previously

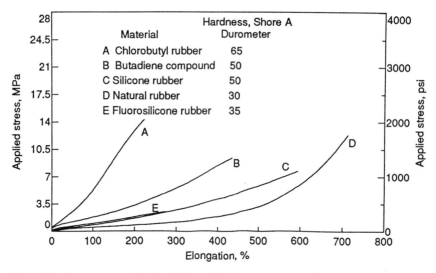

Fig 1. Tensile-test curves for five different elastomer compounds

142

unstressed specimen to the point of rupture, which results in a stress-strain curve of some particular shape. The degree of nonlinearity and in fact complexity of that curve will vary substantially from compound to compound.

In Fig 1, tensile-test curves from five very different compounds, covering a range of base polymer types and hardnesses, are displayed. The contrasts in properties are clearly visible, such as the high elongation (>700%) of the soft natural rubber compound compared with the much lower (about 275%) elongation of a soft fluorosilicone compound. Tensile strengths as low as 2.4 MPa (350 psi) and as high as 15.5 MPa (2.25 ksi) are observed. Different shapes in the curves can be seen, most noticeably in the pronounced curvature of the natural rubber compound.

Figure 2 demonstrates that, even within a single elastomer type, contrasting tensile-property responses will exist. All four of the compounds tested were based on polychloroprene, covering a reasonably broad range of hardnesses, 40 to 70 Shore A Durometer. Contrasts are again seen, but more in elongation levels than in final tensile strength.

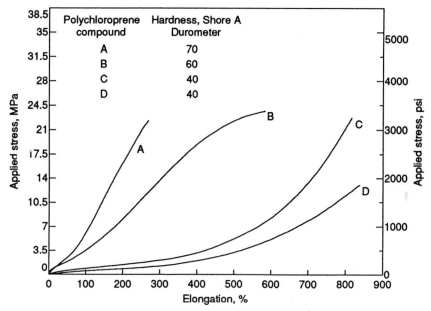

Fig 2. Tensile-test curves for four polychloroprene compounds

Tensile Testing

Two of the compounds are at the same Durometer level, and still display a noticeable difference between their respective stress-strain curves. This shows how the use of differing ingredients in similar formulas can result in some properties being the same or nearly the same whereas others vary substantially.

It should be noted that successive strains to points just short of rupture for any given compound will yield a series of progressively different stress-strain curves; therefore, the tensile-strength rating of a compound would certainly change depending on how it was flexed prior to final fracture.

Thus, the real meaning of rubber tensile strength as determined using the official procedures is open to some question. However, some minimum level of tensile strength is often used as a criterion of basic compound quality, because the excessive use of inexpensive ingredients to fill out a formulation and lower the cost of the compound will dilute the polymer to the point that tensile strength decreases noticeably. For example, neoprene compounds are capable of achieving tensile strengths up to 20.7 MPa (3.0 ksi) or higher when compounded using good technical practice.

In many cases, use of legitimate compounding techniques to optimize specific performance characteristics will result in neoprene compounds whose tensile strengths range from 10.3 to 17.2 MPa (1.5 to 2.5 ksi). The fact that the range has a lower end well below 20.7 MPa (3.0 ksi) does not in any way imply that the compounds are deficient in some sense, but it is generally accepted that a tensile strength of a neoprene compound below 10.3 MPa (1.5 ksi) is evidence that the compound is low in polymer content and therefore its ability to provide good performance over time is questionable.

Various specifications on elastomers, including government and industrial standards, call for minimum tensile strengths at different levels for different types of polymers. Such minima range from perhaps 4.8 MPa (700 psi) for silicones to over 21 MPa (3.0 ksi) for urethanes.

Because elastomeric elements are hardly ever used in tension, tensile strength of compounds is not a useful property measurement for predicting performance. Also, because tensile strength does not correlate with other important characteristics such as stress relaxation and fatigue resistance, it is principally used as a quality-control parameter relating to consistency.

Elongation is the unique defining property of elastomers, and its meaning is somewhat more applicable to end uses. However, because service conditions normally do not require the rubber to stretch to any significant fraction of its ultimate elongative capacity, ultimate elongation still does not provide a precise indication of serviceability.

It is commonly accepted that as the elongation of a compound declines, that material's ability to tolerate strain, including repetitive strain, generally decreases. Thus, if two compounds based on the same elastomer but having quite contrasting elongation values are compared in fatigue properties when both are subjected to equal strain levels, the formula with the higher elongation might well be expected to have the longer life.

Just as with tensile strength, certain minimum levels of ultimate elongation are often called out in specifications for elastomers. The particular elongation required will relate to the type of polymer being used and the stiffness of the compound. For example, a comparatively hard (80 Durometer) fluoroelastomer might have a requirement of only 125% elongation, whereas a soft (30 Durometer) natural rubber might have a minimum required elongation of at least 400%.

Tensile modulus, better described as the stress required to achieve a defined strain, is a measurement of a compound's stiffness. When the stress-strain curve of an elastomer is drawn, it can be seen that the tensile modulus is actually a secant modulus—that is, a line drawn from the graph's origin straight to the point of the specific strain. However, if an engineer really needs to understand what forces will be required to deform the elastomer in a small region about that strain, he or she would be better off drawing a line tangent to the curve at the specific level of strain, and using the slope of that line to determine the approximate ratio of stress to strain in that region. This technique can be utilized in regard to actual elastomeric components as well as lab specimens.

The property of tension set is used as a rough measurement of the compound's tolerance of high strain. This property is not tested very often, but for some particular applications such a test is considered useful. It could also be used as a quality-control measure or compound development tool, but most of the types of changes it will detect in a compound will also show up in tests of tensile strength, elongation, and other properties, and so its use remains infrequent.

Summary

Tensile properties of elastomers vary widely, depending on the particular formulation, and scatter both within and between laboratories is appreciable compared with scatter in tensile testing of metal alloys. ASTM D 412 is the defining specification, and presents detailed instructions on specimen preparation, equipment, test conditions, etc. The meaning of the data is comparatively limited in regard to the utility of any compound for a specific application. Tensile-test data are used effectively as quality-control parameters and general development tools for the rubber technologist.

7

Tensile Testing of Ceramics and Ceramic-Matrix Composites

David Lewis III, Composites and Ceramics Branch,
Naval Research Laboratory

Overview

Rationale for Use of Ceramics

Ceramics (noncomposite ceramics subsequently will be referred to as monolithic ceramics) and ceramic-matrix composites (CMCs) have been shown to have significant potential as structural materials. This is especially true for various specialized applications—particularly those involving high use temperatures. Ceramic materials have several real or potential advantages for such specialized applications that make them very appealing and possibly very competitive with existing structural materials. These advantages include the fact that ceramics can be made from noncritical raw materials (for example, aluminum, boron, carbon, nitrogen, oxygen, silica, and so on), in contrast to the scarce materials (nickel, cobalt, chromium, niobium, and so on) required for high-temperature superalloys. Another advantage is a potential for low cost, based in part on low-cost raw materials. Other advantages are based on the intrinsic properties characteristic of ceramics, including high stiffness (elastic modulus), high hardness, low thermal expansion, low density, chemical stability, thermal stability, and good electromagnetic properties (which are important for electromagnetic windows and electronic materials). The combination of low density, high stiffness, high strength and toughness (in composites), high use temperature, and chemical stability make some ceramics and CMCs most appealing as high-temperature structural materials. In such applications, these materials can be expected to have properties such as stiffness-to-weight and strength-to-weight ratios that far surpass those achievable with competitive materials such as superalloys or intermetallics (for example, NiAl).

Intrinsic Limitations of Ceramics

Unfortunately, some of the desirable intrinsic properties of ceramics also lead to some highly undesirable characteristics. The most significant of these derives from the ionic/covalent bonding typical of most ceramics, which severely limits plastic deformation. This limited plasticity greatly reduces the energy absorbed during fracture. The fracture energy then approaches the very low values of the cleavage energy. The low fracture energy or fracture toughness further results in several undesirable traits. Monolithic ceramics are typically flaw-sensitive, failing as a result of defects that are undetectable by conventional NDE techniques. The same flaw sensitivity also gives rise to great variability in strength, as a result of variations in the flaw population, and thus very low values of design strength. The low fracture energy also implies that monolithic ceramics will typically fail catastrophically—i.e., they will exhibit no stable crack propagation below the critical stress-intensity value, K_{Ic}. The effect here is most severe with respect to the tensile properties of ceramics. Ceramics typically are much higher in compressive strength than in tensile strength, and do not fail in shear modes, because K_{IIc} and K_{IIIc} are much higher than K_{Ic}.

As a result of the severe flaw sensitivity, lack of plastic deformation and relatively high stiffness of ceramics, the tensile strengths of ceramics are typically measured indirectly, rather than in direct tensile tests, as is common for other engineering materials. The results of direct tensile tests are relatively clear, assuming that failure occurs in appropriate locations and modes. In that case, the strength value derived from a direct uniaxial tensile test reflects the true tensile strength of the material. For most ceramics, however, "tensile" strength is measured indirectly by one of two types of flexural or bending tests. In these tests, the specimen is subjected to a complex stress state including tension, compression, shear, and significant stress gradients. In interpreting the results of these flexure tests, the maximum tensile stress present in the specimen at failure is usually reported as the "tensile" strength of the ceramic. Although such testing is straightforward, and calculation of the failure stress simple, many complications are involved. This is particularly true with fiber-reinforced CMCs, for which the results can be very misleading in terms of the true tensile strength of the material tested.

In addition to the widely used flexure tests (three-point, or modulus of rupture, and four-point), there are also other indirect tensile tests, each with its advantages and disadvantages, as will be discussed. Most of these tests have been developed with the intention of overcoming some of the difficulties associated with direct tensile tests or the complications inherent in flexure tests. In addition, especially in recent years, some modifications of tensile-test fixtures and specimens have become available, which make direct tensile testing of some ceramics more tractable.

Effects of Flaw Type and Location on Tensile Tests

One of the complications of tensile testing is the physical location of the flaws that lead to failure. Most ceramics (and other materials) contain both surface and volume flaws. Surface flaws typically result from finishing operations and/or damage during service (for example, damage by foreign objects). Volume flaws typically are intrinsic to the material microstructure or are processing defects (voids, inclusions, etc.). It is important that any "tensile" test characterize the effects of all of these defects (or at least the most severe in terms of performance) on strength. Unfortunately, many of the indirect tensile tests, including flexure tests, produce severe stress gradients that may bias failure toward one type of flaw, most typically toward surface defects. Thus a flexure test on a ceramic material may detect primarily the flaws associated with the machining required to produce the test specimen, rather than the volume flaws associated with the processing of the material. It is quite important here, in trying to assess the "tensile" strength of a material, to be aware of these different flaw types and locations, and their effects on the results of different test procedures.

Separation of Flaw Populations

Assessment of the importance of different types and locations of flaws ideally is based on identification of the actual flaw types using fractography (Ref 1, 2). This is generally a time-consuming and sometimes very difficult task, especially if scanning electron microscopy is required. An alternative although less deterministic approach is to use data-analysis procedures suitable for separating multimodal distributions of strength data into their constituent parts. In some cases, this can be done effectively, although some uncertainties are always associated with this purely mathematical approach to separating the effects of different flaw populations in a material.

Fractography, as performed on ceramics and some ceramic composites, is typically done using reflected light microscopy for the larger flaws, but more often requires scanning electron microscopy for resolution of the small flaws (10 to 30 μm, or 0.39 to 1.2 mils) that are typical of monolithic ceramics. For many ceramics, fractography also requires considerable skill and experience, although there are some efforts underway to standardize this procedure (Ref 1).

Many data-analysis procedures for characterizing strength distributions can be found in the applied mathematics and statistics literature. Commercial computer programs that perform some types of data analysis are widely available, although there are some pitfalls here as well. Different techniques for fitting the same distribution function to a set of data can produce different results for both the function's parameters and the errors in the parameters. These differences can then lead to problems with the use of the strength data, such as with lifetime predictions, predictions of failure probabilities, or estimates of scale effects on strength.

Design Strength and Scale Effects

For ceramics, determination of design strength and prediction of scale effects are two of the most important uses of strength data and thus two of the most important reasons for performing some type of tensile testing and the associated data analysis. For the designer, one of the key requirements is the specification of design strength as a function of service conditions (temperature and environment) and time. Presumably, the designer can specify quite accurately these service conditions (stress, temperature, and so on) as well as the desired lifetime of the component. Thus, accurate and hopefully conservative design-strength values can be incorporated into design codes to help ensure that components will perform as desired.

One aspect of the design process that is more significant for ceramics than for other, less brittle materials is the effect of specimen or component size on strength. The qualitative effect here is that larger specimens or components, on average, will have lower strengths and less scatter in strength values than small specimens. This results from presence in the larger components of greater numbers of flaws and a greater probability of the presence of more severe flaws. If design-strength data based on testing of relatively small specimens are to be used for predicting the performance of larger components, it is necessary to account for the scale effect on strength. This is typically done through the use of Weibull strength distributions, which were developed in the 1940s (Ref 3-5) and have since been widely used for characterizing a variety of material and component properties. Note that variations in size between laboratory test specimens and actual components can be quite large, with very large effects on design strengths. The difference in stressed volume between a metal tensile-test specimen and a solid-fuel rocket-motor casing, and the difference in gage length between a laboratory tensile-test specimen of an optical fiber and a transatlantic communication cable, both may be on the order of 10^6. Because testing of actual components in these and other cases is clearly impractical, accurate and conservative techniques for predicting such scale effects on strength and other significant properties are essential.

Lifetime Predictions and Environmental Effects

An issue that is also related to the nature of flaw and strength distributions is the prediction of component lifetimes from initial strength distributions and knowledge of service conditions. This relies

151

even more heavily on accurate knowledge of the nature of the initial flaw distribution, because the nature of subsequent delayed failure depends strongly on the type and location of the initial flaw that leads to failure. Surface flaws can easily react with the environment, leading to delayed failure in modes such as stress-corrosion cracking. Volume flaws may be stable and may not lead to delayed failure under long-term loading. However, such flaws may also react with the remainder of the material—for instance, with an inclusion that differs chemically from the rest of the material—or may react with the environment diffusing into the bulk of the material. Such changes in volume flaws may subsequently lead to failure of the material. It is clearly important to have detailed knowledge of the nature of the initial flaw population, the manner in which the flaws evolve during service, how they interact with the service environment and the applied loads, and which of them control the service life of the material.

Tensile-Testing Techniques

Direct Tensile Tests

Tensile-testing techniques, as applied to ceramics and ceramic-matrix composites, fall into four basic categories, each of which has its own advantages, problems, and complications. These categories are: (1) true direct tensile tests; (2) indirect tensile tests; (3) other tests where failure is presumed to result from tensile stresses, and (4) the special case of high-temperature tensile tests. Figure 1 illustrates specimen configurations for direct tensile tests. Tests of the other categories will be discussed subsequently.

In terms of analysis of test results, the most straightforward tests are the direct tensile tests. In these tests, the gage length of the specimen is nominally in a state of uniaxial tensile stress. Consequently, both the volume and surface of the gage length are subject to the same simple stress state, which is assumed to be constant throughout the gage volume; that is, it is normally assumed that both the surface and the volume of the gage section of the test specimen are subjected to a state of uniform uniaxial tension. In these tests there are two basic types of specimen geometries, both of which have advantages and disadvantages.

One type of specimen that can be prepared using readily available machine tools is the flat or "dog-bone" specimen (Fig 1a). Such specimens can be prepared readily using milling machines with carbide tooling for some materials and diamond tooling for others. It is also

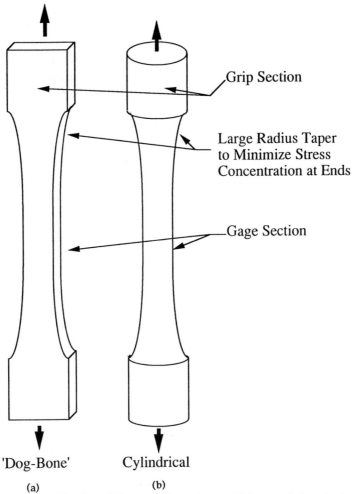

'Dog-Bone'   Cylindrical

(a)   (b)

Fig 1. (a) Flat plate or "dog-bone" direct tensile specimen with large ends for gripping and reduced gage section. (b) Cylindrical tensile specimen with straight ends for collet grips and reduced gage section. Tapers and radii at corners of both specimens may be critical, as is machining finish.

feasible, in some cases, to mold specimens directly into the desired shape (for example, by injection molding), which permits testing of materials with as-fabricated surfaces. These may be preferable to the machined surfaces typical of specimens prepared by grinding, where actual components are not surface finished.

The other type of specimen normally used (Fig 1b) is a cylindrical specimen, typically with a reduced gage section and ends machined to suit some gripping arrangement. Such specimens are typically prepared (in the case of metals and polymers) by machining to the desired shape on a template-controlled profile lathe. In the case of ceramics and CMCs, the analogous procedure uses diamond grinding in the same mode to produce a cylindrical specimen of the desired shape. Again, it is possible, and sometimes desirable, to produce such specimens directly by a molding process, or by machining in the green state prior to firing, when an as-fired surface finish is appropriate for testing. Note that actual specimen shapes may be significantly more complex than those shown schematically in Fig 1; see Fig. 2(e) for the specification for an actual buttonhead tensile specimen.

Gripping and Load Transfer in Direct Tensile Tests. Gripping of both flat and cylindrical specimens can be accomplished in various manners, depending on the particular material being tested. Success in using various gripping techniques will depend on the relative values of tensile strength, shear strength, hardness, and so on, of the material being tested. The dog-bone specimens can be gripped in conventional mechanical grips (Fig 2a) or hydraulic or pneumatic grips (Fig 2b), using friction alone to transmit the load to the specimen. Conventional mechanical wedge-action grips (Fig 2c) can also be used successfully in some cases, although the high and uncontrollable clamping pressure may result in crushing or shear failure in the grip section for some materials. Pneumatic or hydraulic grips are generally preferable, because the gripping pressure can be controlled precisely, and because deformation of the specimen does not produce any change in the gripping pressure.

The success in load transfer through friction depends on achieving a reasonable friction coefficient between the specimen and the grip faces without causing the specimen to fail in compression. As an illustration of this, consider gripping a cylindrical aluminum oxide specimen with a 6.4 mm (0.25 in.) diameter in the gage section and a 12.7 mm (0.5 in.) diameter smooth shank. If the tensile strength is assumed to be

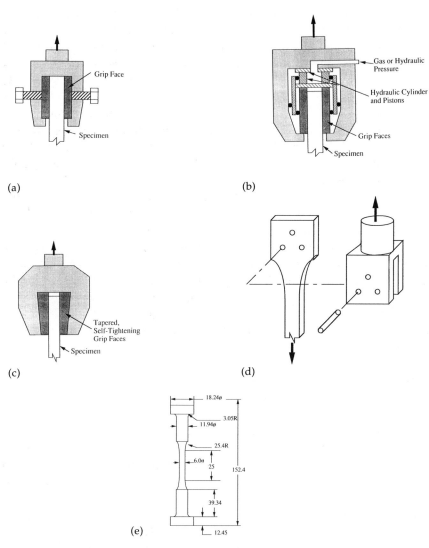

Fig 2. Gripping systems for direct tensile tests. (a) Mechanical grips with screw clamping. (b) Pneumatic (or hydraulic) grips with force applied through lever arrangement and pneumatic pressure, ensuring constant clamping force. (c) Wedge-action, self-tightening mechanical grips; clamping pressure is roughly proportional to the tensile load in the specimen. (d) Pinned grips with load transfer by means of pins through grip and specimen. (e) Specimen configuration (buttonhead) for self-aligning commercial grip systems (all dimensions in millimeters; ground surface finish, 2 to 3 μm).

155

approximately 350 MPa (50 ksi), a tensile test will require a load of 10,900 N (2450 lbf) to fracture the specimen. With a coefficient of friction of 0.13 between the specimen and the grip faces, the lateral clamping force would have to be 83,980 N, or 18,880 lbf ($F=\mu N$). This clamping force is easily achievable with commercially available hydraulic grips.

The compressive stress on the shank of the specimen is based on the area of the specimen surface inserted into the grip. For this example, if the specimen is inserted into the grip to a depth of 25 mm (1 in.), the compressive stress is about 83 MPa (12 ksi), or well within the capability of the material.

It is very important to verify that the specimen geometry of the material being tested is appropriate for that material's strength. A combination of reducing the cross-sectional area of the gage section and increasing the length of insertion into the grips may be necessary to allow frictional gripping on some ceramic materials. If these specimen geometry enhancements are not possible because of limitations in the material, the use of frictional gripping may not be appropriate.

The problems of frictional gripping are generally severe for most ceramics, which typically have high hardnesses and low friction coefficients against other hard materials. This gripping technique is also particularly difficult with some fiber-reinforced CMCs, which combine high tensile strength, high hardness, and low shear strength. The problems are doubly complicated for the CMCs because the low shear strength limits the load transfer, as well as providing the possibility of shear failure in the grip section at high gripping pressures. There is a relatively simple technique for minimizing these problems with CMCs, namely the use of large ratios of grip area to gage section cross-sectional area; however, this technique introduces other problems as well, primarily in terms of the effects of machining damage on the relatively large surface area of the gage section versus the intrinsic flaws in the relatively small volume of a highly reduced gage section.

Gripping of cylindrical specimens can also be done by means of friction, using wedge-type or collet grips, but this involves the same problems as those detailed above, plus the additional difficulties of requiring precise machining of specimen ends to mate with collets, and strict requirements in regard to specimen straightness. In the case of tapered specimen ends, which are used to increase load transfer, or in the case of the buttonhead specimen discussed below, machining can be even more critical.

Load transfer for flat plate or dog-bone specimens can also be effected by means of pins inserted through the grip section of the specimen (Fig 2d), or such pinned ends can be combined with frictional gripping. Load transfer through pins requires, again, a balance between the load that can be transmitted through the bearing area, $\sigma_b A_b$, and the load required to produce tensile failure, $\sigma \cdot A_{gage}$. In most cases, this requires the use of multiple pins for load transfer. The use of multiple pins requires great precision both in the test apparatus and in machining of the specimen (precise hole location and diameter to ensure equal distribution of loading).

One approach sometimes taken to overcome some of these difficulties in specimen gripping and load transfer is bonding of the ceramic or composite specimen to grips of a more forgiving material. A low-shear-strength, high-tensile-strength, unidirectional CMC specimen can be bonded to metallic grips that are a good match for the CMC in terms of Young's modulus (to minimize stress concentration). Provided that sufficient gripping area is available for load transfer through the adhesive, there is then little difficulty in applying load by conventional means to the now-metallic gripping area of the specimen (note that conventional epoxy adhesives have shear strengths that exceed those of some continuous-fiber CMCs). This procedure, which works very well, unfortunately is not useful for the more important high-temperature tensile tests, as will be discussed later.

The last technique to be discussed here is one that has come into use in commercial test fixtures for tensile testing of ceramics, based on a system developed by personnel at Oak Ridge National Laboratory (Ref 6-8). These test fixtures utilize complex systems for eliminating some of the major sources of errors in tensile testing of ceramics with low strains to failure. Both use what is referred to as a "buttonhead" specimen (see Fig. 2e), to which the load is transferred through enlarged regions on the specimen ends. Although these specimens have operational advantages, such as minimal requirements for specimen alignment in the test fixtures, there are severe restrictions on the amount of load that can be transmitted through the buttonhead. The result has been that this type of gripping/load transfer has been very successful with materials of moderate tensile strength, and with long-term, low-stress tests such as creep and stress-rupture tests, but tends to fail for materials with high tensile strengths. Theoretical analysis of the requirements and limitations of this test are extremely difficult, as a result of the complex contact-stress problem at the buttonhead/grip interface. Thus, little guidance, aside from practical experience, can be utilized for determining when this type of test will be successful, and when the large investment in the grips themselves is appropriate.

Experimental Problems and Errors. One major source of error that is inherent in direct tensile tests has been eliminated to a major extent by the introduction of self-aligning grip systems. This error is associated

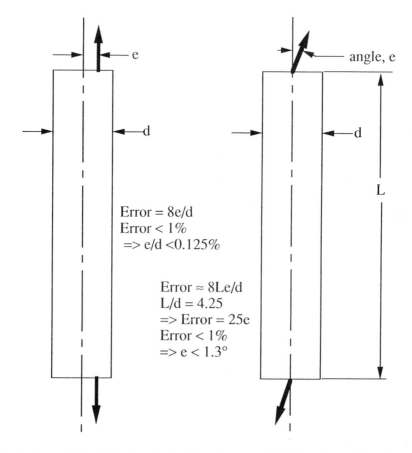

Fig 3. Errors in tensile testing derived from load applied off-center and at angle to centerline of gage section; errors for two effects combined are roughly additive.

with eccentricities in load application (see Fig 3), which lead to a combined state of tension and bending in the test specimen. The large magnitudes of the parasitic bending stresses, even for small degrees of misalignment, result in significant errors in the calculated tensile stress (based on a state of pure tension). However, the use of various types of self-aligning grips, together with appropriate specimen geometries and careful specimen preparation, have largely eliminated these errors (Ref 8). The current self-aligning grips, available from the two major testing-machine manufacturers, use compact hydraulic systems to accomplish the same effect previously achieved through large and costly gas-bearing tensile-test fixtures. The only difficulties with these grip systems are noted above, involving specimen preparation, testing of high-strength materials, and the relatively high cost of the grips.

To some extent, the testing problems for certain continuous-fiber CMCs have been alleviated. This is particularly true for those CMCs that have relatively high strain to failure (for ceramics) and relatively low modulus. In many cases, the simple gripping techniques used for metals and polymers will suffice for such CMCs, and few special precautions need to be taken, aside from ensuring sufficient gripping area relative to the cross-sectional area of the gage section (see the discussion above on gripping). The author has, without great difficulty, performed tensile tests on conventional dog-bone specimens of CMCs, using ordinary pneumatic grips with smooth grip faces made of materials slightly less hard than the CMC itself (for example, aluminum, copper, or silver) and appropriately sized grip and gage areas. Such results suggest that direct tensile testing of advanced CMCs may be far less difficult than testing of monolithic ceramics, and may not require the specialized test fixtures and specimens needed for testing of monolithic ceramics.

Summary of Direct Tensile Tests. The advantages and limitations of direct tensile testing of ceramics and ceramic composites are very clear. The advantages are:

1. Direct measurement of the tensile strength in a known and simple stress state

2. Stressing of the entire gage-section volume and surface, sampling both surface and volume flaws in the material being tested

The disadvantages and limitations include:

1. The need for large specimens (because of the need for large gripping areas)

2. Complex and precise specimen machining requirements for collet grips and especially for buttonhead specimens

3. The need for relatively expensive (and bulky) test fixtures and grips

Indirect Tensile Tests

Indirect tensile tests are few in number and quite similar, typically involving some complex specimen geometry that induces a state of uniaxial tension in a portion of a specimen loaded in a fairly simple manner. Two examples are the theta specimen test, which is a variant of the diametral compression test discussed below, and the trussed beam test, which is similar to the theta specimen test but involves loading in flexure rather than in compression (see Fig 4a and b). Both of these tests provide the capability for performing what is very close to a direct tensile test, but without the need for expensive tensile-test fixtures. Both are also amenable to use at high temperatures, without the great complications that accompany the use of conventional tensile-testing fixtures and procedures. The primary disadvantages of the theta and trussed beam specimens are the difficulty of machining them, especially with respect to the cutouts, and the problem of flaws introduced through such machining. In some cases, direct molding of specimens in these configurations may be possible, eliminating the machining problem altogether, as well as providing sintering, rather than machined, external surfaces—a possible advantage if actual components are prepared to net shape with no external surface finishing.

It should be noted that a great many other similar tests are possible, limited only by the creativity and ability of the experimenter to fabricate the test specimen and analyze the stress state produced. One such example is shown in Fig 4(c), where a thin layer of material to be tested is used as the skin on the tensile side of a sandwich beam. The only requirement for determining the tensile stress at failure is knowledge of the elastic properties of the skin and core materials, and assurance that failure occurs first in the face sheet loaded in tension. The face sheet on the compressive side can be of virtually any high-strength, high-modulus material with known properties.

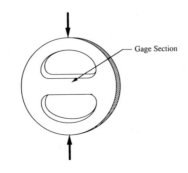

(a)

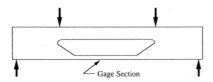

(b)

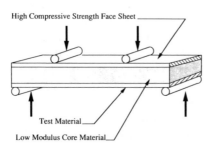

(c)

Fig 4. Specimens for indirect tensile tests. (a) Theta specimen, which provides uniaxial tension for central member when specimen is loaded in diametral compression. (b) Trussed beam specimen, which provides approximately uniaxial tension in lower portion when beam is loaded in four-point bending. (c) Sandwich beam specimen, which loads lower skin in approximately pure bending with four-point flexural loading of beam.

Tensile Testing

Flexure and Other "Tensile" Tests. There are a great variety of other tests used to characterize the tensile strengths of ceramics and ceramic composites, where the gage section of the specimen is not in a state of pure, uniaxial tension, but rather in some combined stress state. Such tests include the three-point and four-point flexure tests commonly used for ceramics, diametral compression tests, C-ring tests, combined-stress-state tests on cylindrical specimens, and various biaxial tests such as ball-on-ring and ring-on-ring tests. When these tests are used to measure tensile strength, it is presumed that there is no effect of combined stresses on failure and that the specimen fails from the largest tensile stress present—that is, the principal tensile stress. Historically, this has been a very good assumption for many monolithic ceramics with low toughness, identical elastic behavior in tension and compression, and essentially linear behavior to failure. However, in the case of many of the tougher ceramic composites, these assumptions are frequently incorrect. Note, however, that the biaxial tests, in some cases, have been used to evaluate the possible dependence of strength on stress state in ceramics.

For many toughening mechanisms present in CMCs, such as phase-transformation toughening, crack bridging, and fiber pullout, the behavior may be stress-state-dependent. In addition, for many such materials, the behavior in tension and the behavior in compression are not equal. The worst case of the latter occurs with some continuous ceramic-fiber composites, in which the compressive failure stress, as a result of fiber buckling, may be substantially lower than the tensile strength. The continuous-fiber CMCs also exhibit, for unidirectional materials, extremely low values of shear strength. This poses the additional problem of possible shear failure in tests where significant shear stresses are present, such as the three-point flexure test and the C-ring test. At present, the only solution to this problem is the careful monitoring of tests to determine the actual mode of failure (for example, compression, shear, or tension). The author and others accomplish this by means of video and telemicroscopic recording of specimen failure processes.

In addition to the difficulties encountered in testing of fiber CMCs, there is the problem of the effects of shear stresses and combined stress states on phenomena such as the martensitic phase transformation used to toughen zirconia alloys and zirconia-containing composites. This phase transformation is primarily a shear transformation, with substantial volume increase as well. Thus, a stress state with a high dilatational stress and high shear stresses may result in a high degree of phase transformation, with consequent effects on the measured "tensile" stress, in contrast to the behavior that might be seen in a direct tensile test with lower dilatational stress and no shear.

Of these various "tensile" tests, by far the most commonly used are the three- and four-point flexure tests. A detailed analysis of the errors that occur in the four-point flexure test (the preferred test; see Fig 5a) has been performed (Ref 9,10), and standards have been developed (Ref 11) for the use of these tests for monolithic ceramics, together with recommendations for both test-specimen geometry and test fixturing. These will not be repeated here, but experience has shown that use of the recommended specimen geometry and test fixtures provides very good characterization of the tensile strengths of monolithics in which strength is controlled by surface flaws. It is also feasible, as with some of the other tests noted, to conduct such tests at high temperature, using appropriate materials for the test fixtures, although many other complications then arise, as will be discussed subsequently. One difficulty with these flexure tests occurs in the presence of stress gradients, with maximum stress occurring at the surface, leading to preferential failure from surface flaws. Another is the presence of shear stresses in regions of the specimen, which is a problem with some materials relatively weak in shear. A third is the presence of compressive stresses as well, which constitute an additional problem for materials, as noted, that fail in compression first. A last problem, which may be handled analytically if sufficient information is available about material response, is the problem of different stress-strain behavior in tension and compression. In the case of the flexure testing of fiber CMCs, matrix microcracking at a low stress level leads to an effective decrease in modulus in a portion of the tensile region of the specimen. This in turn leads to a shift in the neutral axis away from the tensile surface and a redistribution of stresses. In this particular case, use of the conventional beam-bending equations for maximum tensile stress may produce significant errors in the calculated stresses (Ref 12).

Another test, which has been used to a lesser extent, is the C-ring test (Fig 5b), which is especially convenient for testing of materials produced in the form of thin-wall tubes, such as ceramic heat exchangers. In such cases, a slice is taken from the tube, with a portion removed as shown in Fig 5b, and is tested in either tension or compression. Testing in tension produces bending and tensile stresses in the interior of the specimen, as shown, whereas compressive testing similarly stresses the exterior of the specimen in tension. Relatively simple test fixturing suffices to load the specimen in either case, and extension to high temperatures is also relatively simple. This test has been analyzed theoretically (Ref 13-15), and the results presumably are accurate except for the same limitations of the other flexure tests. These include, as above, the problems of stress gradients, failure from surface flaws, and the pres-

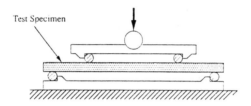

Test Specimen

MTL 4-Point Flexure Test with Roller Loading of
Rectangular Cross-Section Specimen

(a)

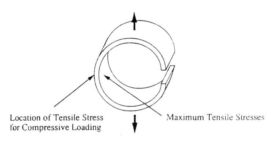

Location of Tensile Stress
for Compressive Loading

Maximum Tensile Stresses

C-Ring Test for 'Tensile' Strength
of Tube Segments

(b)

Fig 5. Other "tensile" tests. (a) Four-point flexure test, which loads lower part of central portion of beam in tension, with a stress gradient in the vertical direction. (b) C-ring test, which provides flexural loading of a segment of a tubular component. (c) Diametral compression, or "Brazilian," test, which produces equal tensile and compressive stresses at the center of the specimen loaded in diametral compression. (d) Cylindrical specimen internally and externally pressurized and mechanically loaded in tension and compression, which can produce any desired combination of tensile and compressive stresses in the hoop and axial directions.

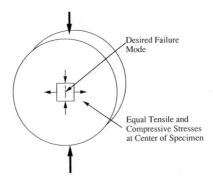

Diametral Compression or 'Brazilian' Test

(c)

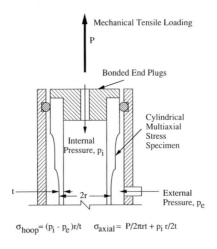

$\sigma_{hoop} = (p_i - p_e)r/t \qquad \sigma_{axial} = P/2\pi rt + p_i r/2t$

(d)

Fig 5. Other "tensile" tests (Continued). (a) Four-point flexure test, which loads lower part of central portion of beam in tension, with a stress gradient in the vertical direction. (b) C-ring test, which provides flexural loading of a segment of a tubular component. (c) Diametral compression, or "Brazilian," test, which produces equal tensile and compressive stresses at the center of the specimen loaded in diametral compression. (d) Cylindrical specimen internally and externally pressurized and mechanically loaded in tension and compression, which can produce any desired combination of tensile and compressive stresses in the hoop and axial directions.

Other tests that have been used for measuring the "tensile" strengths of ceramics include various biaxial flexure tests (ball-on-ring, ring-on-ring) (Ref 16-18) that are equivalent to the three- and four-point flexure tests. These tests are convenient for materials that normally are available in the appropriate geometries—for example, thin plates or disks. These tests are very similar in most ways to the other flexure tests, except that the stress state is roughly equibiaxial, thus stressing flaws of all orientations, rather than only those oriented in the worst direction relative to the maximum tensile stress, as in a conventional flexure test.

Another type of test that is not widely used in the technical ceramics community, but more so in the geological area and with building materials, is the diametral compression, or "Brazilian," test, which uses a disk or short cylinder loaded in compression across its diameter (see Fig 5c). In this test, the maximum tensile stresses are developed at the center of the specimen, where equal tensile and compressive stresses are present as shown. In a successful test of this type, the specimen fails by splitting vertically at its center. This test is particularly useful for materials such as cores from rock sampling, test cylinders of concrete, and similar materials. Typically, exact interpretation of the results in terms of the tensile strength of the material is difficult, because of the difficulty of determining the exact source of failure (from the machined surfaces or from the bulk of the material). There is also the problem, for some materials, of the presence of an equal compressive stress at the center of the specimen, which leads to the development of very large shear stresses at this site. Materials with relatively low shear strengths may thus fail first in shear, rather than in tension.

Combined-Stress-State Tests Using Multiaxial Cylindrical Specimens. The last type of "tensile" test to be discussed in this section is the combined-stress-state test employing multiaxial cylindrical specimens. These specimens (Fig 5d), which can be loaded by various combinations of internal pressure, external pressure, axial tension or compression, and (when desired) torsion, are well suited to production of almost any desired stress state in the cylinder wall. As such, they have been used to address the problem of the failure criteria for brittle materials through systematic variation of the relative proportions and signs of the principal stresses. However, the major difficulties that are inherent in both preparation and use of such specimens have precluded their wide application. These tests require large amounts of material, extensive machining of specimens—typically with a profile lathe and diamond toolpost grinders for ceramics—and elaborate test fixturing. The extensive machining that is required, in addition to greatly increasing the cost of testing, introduces the potential for failure to be initiated by machining-induced flaws, rather than by volume flaws produced during processing. Such tests also have severe limitations with regard to high-temperature testing, as a consequence of the required loading arrangements.

Summary of the Advantages and Limitations of Flexure and Other "Tensile" Tests. The flexural and other indirect "tensile" tests described above provide several advantages over direct tensile tests for ceramic and ceramic composite specimens. These include:

1. Simple specimen geometries, minimal specimen machining and simple test fixturing (flexure, biaxial, diametral compression, and C-ring tests)

2. Use of as-fabricated materials (C-ring test)

3. Capability for testing various stress states (flexure for tension, shear; biaxial flexure and cylindrical multiaxial specimens for combined stress states)

The particular disadvantages of these indirect tensile tests include:

1. Extensive specimen preparation for multiaxial cylindrical specimens

2. Stress gradients and combined stress states that may affect failure modes, especially in ceramic-matrix composites, or in other materials that are relatively weak in shear or exhibit different stress-strain behaviors in tension and compression

High-Temperature Tensile Tests

High-temperature tensile tests pose several specific difficulties and involve several specific requirements for both specimens and test fixtures. The particular difficulties depend on the temperature range involved and the atmosphere in which the test is to be conducted. Depending on the test particulars, suitable types of tests may include direct tensile tests, four-point flexure tests, and C-ring tests, the last two of which are subject to complications resulting from the stress states involved. Successful use has also been made of the theta specimen test, although this test has not become particularly popular because of the specimen machining involved.

Hot Grip Tests

The complications that involve the test temperature range are associated with the fixture materials available for transfer of load to the specimen (assuming that these fixtures are in the hot zone of the furnace). The alternative, which poses its own set of problems, is the use of large specimens and grips outside the test furnace. Typical ferrous materials for grips, pullrods, pushrods, loading anvils, and so on, are limited to approximately 1000 to 1200 °C (1830 to 2190 °F) because of severe strength loss at higher temperatures, as well as chemical problems (reaction, oxidation, etc.). The fixture materials suitable for higher-temperature use include various superalloys, which can be used at temperatures up to about 1200 °C (2190 °F), but may be expensive, difficult to machine, and subject to oxidation. Other, even more exotic materials include molybdenum, TZM, thoria-dispersed nickel, and carbon or carbon-carbon composites. Some of these materials—for example, molybdenum and carbon/carbon—can be used at extremely high temperatures (up to about 2000 °C, or 3630 °F), but only in vacuum or inert atmospheres. Ceramics have also been used for high-temperature fixtures and grips, and may generally be used in a range of atmospheres. Unfortunately, some of the applications (for example, pullrods) are limited by the relatively low tensile strengths (200 to 400 MPa, or 30 to 60 ksi) of most of the available ceramics. The use of ceramics is also limited to temperatures of about 1500 to 1700 °C (2730 to 3090 °F) by the ceramics available in suitable forms for test fixtures and grips, such as aluminum oxide, silicon carbide, and silicon nitride. Finally, the use of ceramic grips and fixturing is severely limited by the difficulties and very high cost associated with machining test fixtures from suitable ceramic materials, which are hard and brittle.

Direct Tensile Tests

Assuming the desire to work with hot grips, or hot fixtures, to avoid some of the difficulties associated with cold grips, the selection of tests is very limited. Direct tensile tests can be performed only up to the temperature limitations of the grip materials, assuming that high-temperature-material analogs of one of the grip types have been acquired. This translates into a temperature limitation of about 1000 °C (1830 °F) for typical commercial metallic grips available at reasonable cost. Testing at somewhat higher temperatures can be performed, albeit at great cost, with ceramic analogs of these grips, and testing at temperatures of approximately 2000 °C (3630 °F) is possible with molybdenum grips in an inert atmosphere.

Four-Point Flexure Tests

Relatively appealing alternatives to direct tensile tests include C-ring and four-point flexure tests. Such tests can be readily performed with ceramic fixtures and pushrods, permitting testing in a variety of atmospheres at temperatures up to perhaps 1700 °C (3090 °F). The MTL four-point test fixture, depicted in Fig 5(a), can be duplicated in a variety of ceramics (for example, alumina for the top and bottom anvil supports and pushrods, and sapphire for the loading-anvil rollers) at relatively low cost. Four-point flexure tests of this type can be used quite successfully, provided that some of the complications noted previously (for example, differing stress-strain behavior in compression and tension, and significant effects of shear stresses) do not occur. Another complication that may also arise in high-temperature flexure testing of ceramics is the presence of large strains and deflections resulting from increases in ductility or other flow processes that are operative at high temperatures. Such large strains may produce significant errors in stress values calculated by the use of beam-bending theories based on infinitesimal strains.

C-Ring Test

The C-ring test can also be readily used at high temperatures—particularly if the ring is loaded in compression by means of appropriate ceramic anvils and pushrods (Ref 13, 15). Loading in tension with ceramic attachments and pullrods is also possible, because of the relatively low loads required to cause failure via the bending stresses in this test. This particular test has, in fact, been used quite successfully in the development of ceramics and CMCs for high-temperature heat exchangers, which are fabricated from relatively thin-wall tubes. Attempts to characterize the tensile strengths of such tubes by testing of machined specimens would lead to very misleading results, because in this case specimen strength would be controlled primarily by machining damage, whereas the strength of the actual components, with their as-fabricated surfaces, is controlled by intrinsic defects.

Cold Grip Tests

In the event that it is feasible to work with either cooled grips (inside the furnace) or cold grips (outside the furnace), the tests that are most suitable are quite different. In this case, as shown in Fig 6, any number of grip arrangements can be used, in conjunction with a long specimen, with the gage section contained within the hot zone of the test furnace. Several commercial vendors now offer systems that combine small test furnaces, some with hot zones as short as 2.5 to 5 cm (1 to 2 in.), with self-aligning grips (in some cases, water cooled) for the buttonhead specimens. The author has similarly used a small furnace around the gage section of a long, rectangular CMC tensile specimen gripped on aluminum tabs epoxy bonded to the end of the specimen.

This technique is not without its disadvantages. It requires large amounts of material for test specimens, which are typically more than 15 cm (5.9 in.) in length, and rather expensive test fixtures and furnaces (assuming that commercial equipment is used). Another unavoidable

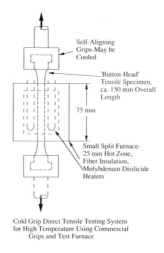

Self-Aligning
Grips-May be
Cooled

'Button-Head'
Tensile Specimen,
ca. 150 mm Overall
Length

75 mm

Small Split Furnace-
25 mm Hot Zone,
Fiber Insulation,
Molybdenum Disilicide
Heaters

Cold Grip Direct Tensile Testing System
for High Temperature Using Commercial
Grips and Test Furnace

Fig 6. Schematic illustration of cold grip tensile-testing arrangement with long specimen gripped outside of compact test furnace; commercial systems in this configuration are available for testing in air at temperatures up to about 1700 °C (3100 °F).

problem with this cold grip technique, and with the use of cooled grips in the furnace hot zone, is that of thermal gradients in the specimen, and increased requirements for power in the test furnace, because of the transfer of heat out of the furnace through the specimen and into the grips. The cold grip technique also poses some problems with control of the atmosphere inside the furnace, because seals must be provided around the test specimen where it passes into the furnace. This is not a major problem with hot grip tests, where very effective seals (for example, high-temperature bellows) can be provided at the points where the pullrods enter the furnace.

Strain Measurement

Historically, measurement of strains has been one of the major problems with high-temperature tensile testing of ceramics by either direct tensile tests or any of the indirect methods. One of the factors contributing to the difficulty of measuring strains in a high-temperature ceramic tensile specimen is the relatively low strain-to-failure in

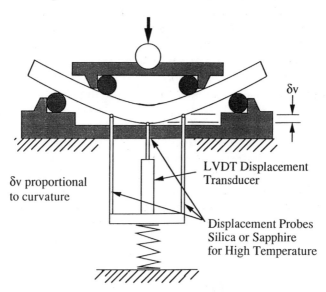

Fig 7. Schematic diagram illustrating three-probe LVDT measurement of curvature of central portion of four-point flexure system. The usual assumption of pure bending between inner load points implies that the strain is proportional to the curvature of the beam. The curvature is proportional to the difference in displacements as sensed directly by the linear variable differential transformer (or other displacement transducer).

ceramics and CMCs. Frequently the maximum tensile strain achieved in monolithics is less than 0.1%, and even in the tough-fiber CMCs, the maximum strain may be only 2 to 3%. Measurement of such small strains is in general a very challenging task, and more so inside a high-temperature test furnace. In the past, the typical techniques used for "strain" measurements have involved measurement of the over-all travel of the load train outside the test furnace or measurement of the elongation or deformation of the specimen by means of displacement transducers coupled to the specimen by refractory rods (Ref 19) (see Fig 7). Also available were dual-channel optical tracking systems capable of tracking two marks or flags on the specimen, thus providing a noncontact and highly precise method of measuring the strain in the gage section of the specimen. However, such optical trackers were extremely expensive, rivaling the cost of a complete test machine, and thus were not used extensively.

The situation with regard to strain measurement has improved dramatically in recent years, and several reasonably priced commercial systems for strain measurement inside high-temperature furnaces are now available (Ref 7, 20). One such system employs suitable extensions (silica, sapphire, silicon carbide, and so on) to the clip gages commonly used to measure strain in ambient-temperature tensile tests. These high-temperature clip gages permit accurate measurement of strain in a chosen portion of the test specimen, requiring only two ports in the side of the furnace for the extension rods. These direct-contact extensometers are available at moderate cost and are capable of measuring displacements and strains with extremely high accuracy.

Also made available quite recently have been various laser-based strain-measurement devices that can be used easily at high temperatures, requiring only a window in the side of the furnace through which the specimen can be sighted. These laser systems work in several distinct ways. One commercial system tracks two flags, as did the optical tracking systems previously mentioned, but offers laser technology and modern electronics at a cost comparable to that of the high-temperature clip gages cited above. The laser systems have the advantage that the radiation from the hot furnace interior does not interfere with the measurement, as it would with an optical tracking system following two marks on a specimen inside a hot furnace. The normal effect at temperatures above approximately 1000 °C (1830 °F) is that everything in the furnace looks the same (color differences are only a function of emissivity). With the use of lasers, the sensors can be equipped with narrow band filters that pass only the laser wavelength. Additionally, the laser signal can be modulated, with the sensors detecting only the modulated, ac signal, and not the dc background from the thermal radiation inside the furnace (helium-neon lasers are roughly the same color as the inside of a furnace at 800 to 900 °C, or 1470 to 1650 °F).

Another system that is amenable to use with a great variety of test specimens, even with extremely small-diameter (10 μm, or 0.4 mil) ceramic fibers, uses the speckle pattern generated by the reflection of a coherent laser beam from the surface of the specimen. As the specimen deforms, the speckle pattern deforms in a similar manner, and measurement of the changes in the speckle pattern permit accurate measurement of the strain in any direction on the surface of the specimen. These speckle interferometric strain gages are also reasonable in cost, easy to use, and require, again, only a sight port or small opening in the test furnace.

With the two types of laser strain gages and the high-temperature clip gage, there is now little difficulty in making direct and precise measurements of strain in high-temperature tensile specimens. With some of the other, indirect tensile tests, there are also relatively convenient ways of measuring strain. For example, for the four-point flexure test, a convenient and very accurate way of measuring strain in the central portion of the test specimen is the use of a three-probe displacement transducer system (see Fig 7), which effectively measures the curvature of the central portion of the beam (which is normally assumed to be in pure bending where the strain is proportional to the curvature). Accordingly, strain measurement is not now considered to be a significant problem in tensile testing of ceramics.

Atmosphere Control in High-Temperature Tensile Tests

Control of the atmosphere in high-temperature tensile tests of ceramics and CMCs continues to be a significant problem. The situation for test temperatures below 1000 to 1200 °C (1830 to 2190 °F) is tractable, in that hot grips, or cooled grips inside the furnace, can be used, with effective seals on the pullrods and little restriction of atmosphere imposed by the grip materials (for example, oxidation of metal grips). However, for temperatures above 1200 °C (2190 °F), the problems are severe. The higher-temperature metallic grips (molybdenum) must be used only in inert or reducing conditions, and grips fabricated from graphite or carbon-carbon composites must be used under inert conditions (vacuum, argon, and so on). If the application requires testing in oxidizing conditions, as would be the case for gas turbine or hypersonic airframe materials, such tests may give very misleading results. High-temperature tests under oxidizing conditions (for example, in air or in simulated gas turbine combustion products) require either ceramic fixtures, which limit the type of test that can be performed and the loads that can be achieved in tensile tests, or the use of cold grips outside the furnace. Use of cold grips requires extremely large specimens (for experimental materials) and is complicated by the problem of sealing the furnace to provide effective atmosphere control. An appealing alternative, in many cases, is the use of four-point flexure tests with ceramic fixtures and pushrods, in which it is possible to test to quite high temperatures (about 1700 °C, or 3090 °F) in a variety of atmospheres ranging from reducing, through inert, to oxidizing conditions. Materials such as aluminum oxide and sapphire (for load points) will survive atmospheres such as forming gas, argon, nitrogen, vacuum, air, and oxygen, with little effect on the test fixturing, even at very high temperatures.

Recommendations for High-Temperature Tensile Testing of Ceramics

In summary, there are some clear choices for high-temperature tensile testing of ceramics, provided that appropriate test equipment and fixturing are affordable. The clear choice for most monolithic ceramics is the use of precisely aligned hydraulic grips or self-aligning grip systems, with straight-shank or buttonhead specimens, a small furnace system, and direct-contact extensometers or optical measurement of the specimen strain. Note that the buttonhead specimens are limited in load levels, as are pinned dog-bone specimens, and may be more suitable for lower stress level tests such as creep and fatigue tests.

A test system such as that described above typically involves an additional expenditure of about $100,000 beyond the cost of a test machine on which to mount the high-temperature test components. Some modification of the gripping arrangement and grips (and some additional expense) may be necessary for testing of high-strength monolithics or CMCs. If test temperatures are always below 1000 °C

(1830 °F), it is possible to use a much less expensive system, employing hot grips and a large furnace.

For situations where neither true tensile-testing system is practical, the most reasonable alternative is the use of the four-point flexure test with displacement transducer measurement of the strain in the central (gage) portion of the specimen. Use of some of the other tests described should be limited to the special cases applications for which they are appropriate (for example, use of the C-ring test for tube segments and the diametral compression tests for cylindrical specimens). The biaxial tests (ball-on-ring and ring-on-ring) may have some limited usefulness in situations where actual loading is biaxial and effects of combined stresses are expected to be significant.

Recommendations for and Summary of Tensile Testing of Ceramics and Ceramic Composites

Recommended Procedures for Ambient-Temperature Tensile Testing of Ceramics and CMCs

Monolithic Ceramics and Low-Toughness CMCs

1. Direct tensile tests using the currently available commercial self-aligning grip systems and strain-measurement techniques. These tests require relatively expensive gripping systems, strain-measurement techniques, and large specimens with complex machining requirements. Specimen geometry has been established for these gripping systems to minimize failure in the gripping or transition regions.

2. Where material availability or economic constraints prevent such testing, four-point flexure testing following the recent ASTM standard; strain measurement preferably is done by measuring the displacement in the central portion of the test specimen at three points.

High-Toughness CMCs and other Ceramics with High Strains to Failure

1. Direct tensile tests using either the self-aligning grip systems or simpler grip systems typically used for metals or polymers; strain measurement by conventional techniques (clip gages) may be adequate. With the use of the more conventional gripping systems, it may be possible to work with flat plate specimens, which may be easier to fabricate.

2. Four-point flexure tests in which the details of the fracture process are observed carefully, to ensure that failure does in fact occur first in a tensile mode, and with corrections for neutral axis shifts resulting from differing tensile and compressive stress-strain behavior.

Specialized Materials (Such as Heat-Exchanger Tubes)

1. Direct tensile tests if sufficiently large specimens can be obtained from components to minimize the effects of surface machining damage.

2. Otherwise, C-ring or other similar tests, with the same careful observation and corrections recommended for the four-point bend test.

Recommended Procedures for High-Temperature Tensile Testing of Ceramics and CMCs

Monolithic Ceramics and Low-Toughness CMCs

1. Direct tensile tests using the currently available commercial self-aligning grip systems, with grips outside a compact furnace, and commercial high-temperature strain-measurement techniques. These tests require relatively expensive gripping systems, strain-measurement techniques, furnace systems, and large specimens with complex machining requirements.

2. Where availability of material or financial limitations make the procedure above impractical, the alternative is four-point flexure with appropriate measurement of strain, as above.

High-Toughness CMCs and other Ceramics with High Strains to Failure

1. Direct tensile tests using either self-aligning cold grip systems or simpler hot grip systems typically used for metals or polymers, with optical or capacitance (clip) gage measurement of strain; again, conventional grips may make it possible to work with the more easily fabricated flat plate or dog-bone specimen.

2. Four-point flexure tests in which the details of the fracture process are observed carefully (this is far more difficult in the confines of a high-temperature furnace), to ensure that failure does in fact occur first in a tensile mode, and with corrections for neutral axis shifts resulting from differing tensile and compressive stress-strain behavior.

Specialized Materials (Such as Heat-Exchanger Tubes)

1. Direct tensile tests if sufficiently large specimens can be obtained from components to minimize the effects of surface machining damage.

2. Otherwise, C-ring or other similar tests, with the same careful observation and corrections recommended for the four-point bend test.

These observations and corrections are difficult to make in a high-temperature test, although C-ring and other indirect tensile tests are otherwise relatively easy to translate to high-temperature tests.

Recommended Procedures for Data Analysis and Reporting: Critical Experimental Parameters and Error Analysis

The recommended procedures for data analysis and reporting are partly covered in the ASTM standards for flexure and tensile testing. What is not covered in the current standards is the desirability, and in many cases the necessity, of performing significant fractographic analyses to identify the flaws leading to failure in the tensile tests. Also not covered in such standards are some of the complexities related to data analysis, such as in the determination of Weibull parameters for experimental strength distributions, or appropriate procedures for dealing with strength distributions that may be multimodal, such as might result from the presence of several discrete flaw populations. To avoid difficulties with such complications, and to make results most useful to others, it is advisable to report, as much as possible, the details of the data-analysis procedures used, and the assumptions used or implicit in the derivation of parameters from the experimental data. The author is currently working on this problem, in conjunction with the need for consistent analysis of strength data for ceramic fiber development programs, and reliable software packages for such data analysis may be available in the near future.

Review of Pertinent Literature

Unfortunately, there is little to offer in the way of summaries or review articles on tensile testing of ceramics and ceramic-matrix composites. The most recent such compendium is the chapter listed below as Ref 19, which was prepared in 1967. Most of the more recent information and results on tensile testing of ceramics and CMCs appear in fragmentary form in various papers and reports. Eventually, the Department of Energy effort (Ref 21) may produce something of value, because the contract includes an effort at the National Institute of Standards and Technology on standardization of tensile tests for ceramics, as well as several other programs on tensile testing. There is also a substantial amount of useful information on various types of specialized tensile testing, including specimen types and gripping arrangements in some reports, such as Ref 22 and 23, and the series of reports put out by United Technologies Research Center on its Office of Naval Research contracts (for example, Ref 24) contain a wealth of information on tensile testing of ceramic-matrix composites. Unfortunately, very few of these results have ever been published in the open literature, but these reports should be readily available from their sponsors.

Annotated References

1. G. Quinn, "Standard Practice for Characterizing Strength Limiting Defects in Advanced Structural Ceramics," proposed ASTM standard for fractography, NIST, Nov 1990. This is a draft standard for fractographic analysis of ceramic materials, including techniques for flaw location and identification.
2. R.W. Rice, Ceramic Fracture Features, Observations, Mechanisms and Uses, *Fractography of Ceramic and Metal Failures*, STP 827, ASTM, 1984, p 5-103. This is a very lengthy and comprehensive article on fractography as applied to ceramics and ceramic composites, and covers most of the information required to apply fractography to analysis of ceramic tensile-test failures.
3. S.B. Batdorf, Fundamentals of the Statistical Theory of Failure, *Fracture Mechanics of Ceramics*, Vol 3, R.C. Bradt, D.P.H. Hasselman, A.G. Evans, and F.F. Lange, Ed., Plenum Press, 1978, p 1-29. This describes a generalization of Weibull distribution functions for characterizing strength distributions, with a discussion of the relationship between flaw distributions and strength-distribution functions.
4. D. Lewis, Curve-Fitting Techniques and Ceramics, *Am. Ceram. Soc. Bull.*, Vol 57 (No. 4), 1978, p 434-437. An analysis of some of the more insidious errors involved in fitting analytical functions to experimental data; the author is currently working on an extension of this effort, including the use of Weibull distribution functions.
5. W. Weibull, A Statistical Distribution Function of Wide Applicability, *J. Appl. Mech.*, Vol 18, 1951, p 293-297. This is the original (English) paper by Weibull on the use of the Weibull distribution function for the chararacterization of a wide range of material and component property data.
6. D.F. Baxter, Jr., Tensile Testing at Extreme Temperatures, *Adv. Mater. Proc.*, Vol 139 (No. 2), 1991, p 22-32. Provides information on currently available test fixtures and furnaces for high-temperature tensile testing, as well as on strain-measurement instrumentation.
7. J.C. Bittence, New Emphasis on Automation, *Adv. Mater. Proc.*, Vol 136 (No. 5), 1989, p 45-56. Information similar to that in Ref 6.
8. K.C. Liu and C.R. Brinkman, Tensile Cyclic Fatigue of Structural Ceramics, *Proc. 23rd Automotive Technology Development Contractor's Coordination Meeting*, Vol

165, Society of Automotive Engineers, Oct 1985, p 279-284. Description of self-aligning hydraulic grips, using the "buttonhead" tensile specimen, as developed at Oak Ridge National Laboratory and recently commercialized.

9. F.I. Baratta and W.T. Matthews, "Errors Associated with Flexure Testing of Brittle Materials," U.S. Army Materials Technology Laboratory Report MTL TR 87-35, 1987. This report provides a detailed analysis of the errors possible in flexure testing of ceramics and provides most of the basis for the flexure test standard (Ref 10).

10. F.I. Baratta, Requirements for Flexure Testing of Brittle Materials, *Methods for Assessing the Structural Reliability of Brittle Materials*, STP 844, ASTM, 1984, p 194-222. Recently developed flexure-test standard that provides excellent guidance for flexure tests of monolithic ceramics.

11. G. Quinn, "Flexural Strength of High Performance Ceramics at Ambient Temperature," Department of the Army, MIL-STD-1942(MR), 1984. Army-developed MIL-STD test specification that preceded the ASTM Special Technical Publication (Ref 10) and that makes slightly different test recommendations.

12. D.B. Marshall and A.G. Evans, Failure Mechanisms in Ceramic Fiber-Ceramic Matrix Composites, *J. Am. Ceram. Soc.*, Vol 68 (No. 5), 1985, p 225-231. Covers some limited efforts on tensile testing of ceramic-matrix composites, together with some detailed analyses of the peculiarities of these materials, including the various failure modes.

13. M.K. Ferber, V.J. Tennery, S. Waters, and J.C. Ogle, Fracture Strength Characterization of Tubular Ceramics Using a Simple C-Ring Geometry, *J. Mater. Sci.*, Vol 8, 1986, p 2628-2632. Description and examples of the use of the C-ring test for characterization of the "tensile" strengths of segments of tubular ceramic materials.

14. O.M. Jadaan, D.L. Shelleman, J.C. Conway,Jr., J.J. Mecholsky, and R.E. Tressler, Prediction of the Strength of Ceramic Tubular Components: Part I—Analysis, *J. Test. Eval.*, Vol 19 (No. 3), 1991, p 181-191. Theoretical analysis of the C-ring test.

15. D.L. Shelleman, O.M. Jadaan, J.C. Conway, Jr., and J.J. Mecholsky, Jr., Prediction of the Strength of Ceramic Tubular Components: Part II—Experimental Verification, *J. Test. Eval.*, Vol 19 (No. 3), 1991, p 192-201. Experimental verification of the theoretical analysis in Ref 14.

16. G. de With and H.H.H. Wagemens, Ball-on-Ring Test Revisited, *J. Am. Ceram. Soc.*, Vol 72 (No. 8), 1989, p 1538-1541. Analysis of ball-on-ring biaxial flexure test, analogous to three-point flexure test, and adaptable to high-temperature use.

17. H. Fessler and D.C. Fricker, A Theoretical Analysis of the Ring-on-Ring Loading Disk Test, *J. Am. Ceram. Soc.*, Vol 67 (No. 9), 1984, p 582-588. An analysis of the ring-on-ring biaxial flexure test, roughly analogous to the four-point test, and readily adaptable to high-temperature testing.

18. D.K. Shetty, A.R. Rosenfield, and W.H. Duckworth, Statistical Analysis of Size and Stress State Effects on the Strength of An Alumina Ceramic, *Methods for Assessing the Structural Reliability of Brittle Materials*, STP 844, ASTM, 1984, p 57-80. Provides some discussion of stress state effects (biaxial versus conventional flexure) and size effects on strength of monolithic ceramics.

19. S.A. Bortz and T.B. Wade, Analysis and Review of Mechanical Testing Procedure for Brittle Materials, *Structural Ceramics and Testing of Brittle Materials*, S.J. Acquaviva and S.A. Bortz, Ed., Gordon and Breach, 1968, p 47-139. Very old but still relevant review of direct and indirect tensile-testing procedures for ceramics, including discussion of high-temperature test methods.
20. Laser Gages Creep of Ceramics, *Adv. Mater. Proc.*, Vol 138 (No. 5), 1990, p 75-76. Information on currently available commercial, noncontact strain-measurement techniques suitable for ceramic tensile tests.
21. Semiannual Progress Reports on Ceramic Technology for Advanced Heat Engines Project, DOE Contract DE-AC05-840R21400, Oak Ridge National Laboratory, D.R. Johnson, Project Manager (1983-present). These reports (there are approximately 18 volumes of 300-400 pages each) provide information on the DOE contracts involving tensile testing of ceramics and the development of standard tensile test procedures (DOE is interested in developing property data bases for structural ceramics).
22. D. Lewis, C. Bulik, and D. Shadwell, Standardized Testing of Refractory Matrix/Ceramic Fiber Composites, *Ceram. Eng. Sci. Proc.*, Vol 6 (No. 7-8), 1985, p 507-523. Broad discussion of suitable test procedures for CMCs.
23. D.C. Larsen, S.L. Stuchly, and J.W. Adams, "Evaluation of Ceramics and Ceramic Composites for Turbine Engine Applications," Final Report on AFWAL/MLLM Contract F33615-82-C-5101, Dec 1988. This report provides examples of successful ambient and elevated-temperature tensile testing of continuous-fiber CMC materials.
24. K.M. Prewo, G.K. Layden, E.J. Minford, and J.J. Brennan, "Advanced Characterization of Silicon Carbide Fiber Reinforced Glass-Ceramic Matrix Composites," interim report dated 30 June 1985, ONR Contract N00014-81-C-0571. This report on the United Technologies Research Center program on Compglas CMCs, and many others, on the ONR contract cited, provides extensive details of both test procedures and test results, and should be available from either ONR or the authors.

Selected References

• H.C. Cao, E. Bischoff, O. Sbaizero, M. Ruhle, A.G. Evans, D.B. Marshall, and J. Brennan, Effects of Interfaces on the Mechanical Properties of Fiber-Reinforced Brittle Materials, *J. Am. Ceram. Soc.*, Vol 73 (No. 6), 1990, p 1691-1699. Covers some limited efforts on tensile testing of ceramic-matrix composites.
• H. Cao and M.D. Thouless, Tensile Tests of Ceramic-Matrix Composites: Theory and Experiment, *J. Am. Ceram. Soc.*, Vol 73 (No. 7), 1990, p 2091-2094. Covers some limited efforts on tensile testing of ceramic-matrix composites.

- J.J. Mecholsky, Evaluation of Mechanical Property Testing Methods for Ceramic Matrix Composites, *Am. Ceram. Soc. Bull.*, Vol 65 (No. 2), 1 986, p 315-322. Broad discussion of both strength and toughness measurement techniques for CMCs, including pinned grips, dog-bone specimens, and specimens with bonded metal tabs.

8

Tensile Testing of Fiber-Reinforced Composites

James M. Whitney, University of Dayton

Tensile testing of fiber-reinforced composite materials is performed for the purpose of determining uniaxial tensile strength, Young's modulus, and Poisson's ratio relative to principal material directions. The unidirectional lamina provides the basic building block of the multi-directional laminate. Therefore, characterization of lamina material properties allows predictions of the properties of laminates. In actual practice, considerable success has been demonstrated in predicting laminate effective modulus or Poisson's ratio from ply properties. However, prediction of laminate strength properties from lamina strength data has proved more difficult, and therefore it is often necessary to resort to characterization of laminate strength properties. Thus, basic tensile testing is divided into lamina and laminate testing. There also are specimen differences between polymeric-matrix and metal-matrix composites that require separate discussions. Basic tensile-test methods for both polymeric-matrix and metal-matrix composites are confined to those materials that behave on the macroscale as orthotropic bodies. Off-axis tensile testing, because of existence of shear coupling, must be considered separately.

Fundamentals of Tensile Testing of Composite Materials

Unlike homogeneous, isotropic materials, fiber-reinforced composites are characterized by properties that are direction-dependent. Advanced composites, whether of the polymeric-matrix class or the metal-matrix class, often are utilized in the form of a laminate. The lamina, or unidirectionally reinforced ply (Fig 1), is the basic building block of the laminate. In order to perform engineering analysis, the heterogeneous lamina consisting of a fiber phase and a matrix phase is treated as a homogeneous, orthotropic material. In addition, laminate modeling assumes that plies are in a state of plane stress.

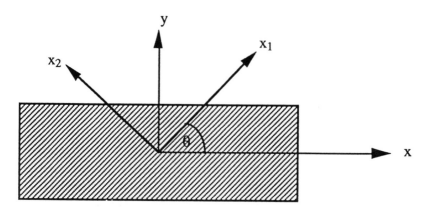

Fig 1. Lamina coordinate system

Stress-Strain Relationships for an Orthotropic Material

Development of stress-strain relationships for an orthotropic material requires the definition of engineering constants. Using Fig 1, the unidirectional material is orthotropic with respect to the x_1-x_2 axes. The stress-strain relationships for plane stress are of the forms

$$\varepsilon_1 = \frac{1}{E_1}\sigma_1 - \frac{v_{12}}{E_1}s_2 \qquad\qquad\qquad \text{(Eq 1a)}$$

$$\varepsilon_2 = -\frac{v_{12}}{E_1}\sigma + \frac{1}{E_1}\sigma_2 \qquad\qquad\qquad \text{(Eq 1b)}$$

$$\gamma_{12} = \frac{1}{G_{12}}\tau_{12} \qquad\qquad\qquad\qquad \text{(Eq 1c)}$$

where, in the usual manner, the normal stresses and strains in the x_1 and x_2 directions are denoted by σ_1, ε_1, σ_2, and ε_2, respectively, whereas the shear stress and strain are denoted by τ_{12} and γ_{12}, respectively. In addition, E_1, E_2, and G_{12} are the Young's modulus parallel to the fibers, the Young's modulus transverse to the fibers, and the shear modulus relative to the x_1-x_2 plane, respectively. The major Poisson's ratio, as determined from contraction transverse to the fibers during a uniaxial test parallel to the fibers, is denoted by v_{12}. For laminates in which the macroscopic stress-strain relationships are orthotropic, Eq 1 is valid, with the subscripts 1 and 2 replaced by x and y, respectively.

Shear Coupling Phenomenon

Components of stress and strain can be transformed from one coordinate system to another. Thus, it is possible to establish the stress-strain relationship in any coordinate system. For the unidirectional composite in Fig 1, the constitutive relationships relative to the x-y coordinate system can be written in the forms

$$\varepsilon_x = \frac{1}{E_x}\sigma_x - \frac{v_{12}}{E_x}\sigma_y + \frac{\eta_x}{E_x}\tau_{xy} \qquad\qquad \text{(Eq 2a)}$$

$$\varepsilon_y = -\frac{v_{xy}}{E_y}\sigma_x + \frac{1}{E_y}\sigma_y + \frac{\eta_y}{E_y}\tau_{xy} \qquad \text{(Eq 2b)}$$

$$\gamma_{xy} = \frac{\eta_x}{E_y}\sigma_x + \frac{\eta_y}{E_x}\sigma_y + \frac{1}{G_{xy}}\tau_{xy} \qquad \text{(Eq 2c)}$$

Equations 2a, b, and c correspond to the stress-strain relationships of an anisotropic material subjected to plane stress. Of particular significance is the fact that the normal strains are coupled to the shear stress and the shear strain is coupled to the normal stresses. Such behavior is referred to as the "shear coupling phenomenon" and requires the definition of two additional elastic properties. In particular, the elastic constants η_x and η_y are shear coupling coefficients determined from uniaxial tensile tests in the x and y directions, respectively—i.e.,

$$\eta_x = \frac{\gamma_{xy}}{\varepsilon_x} \text{ (uniaxial tension in the } x\text{-direction)} \qquad \text{(Eq 3a)}$$

$$\eta_y = \frac{\gamma_{xy}}{\varepsilon_y} \text{ (uniaxial tension in the } y\text{-direction)} \qquad \text{(Eq 3b)}$$

As a result, there are some significant ramifications of this behavior relative to tensile testing that will be discussed in more detail in the section on off-axis test specimens.

Symmetric Laminates and Laminate Notation

As shown in Fig 1, the principal material directions within each ply of a laminate are denoted by an x_1-x_2 axis system. Laminate stacking sequences can be easily described for composites composed of layers of the same material with equal ply thickness by simply listing the ply orientations from the top of the laminate to the bottom. thus, the notation [0°/90°/0°] uniquely defines a three-layer laminate. The angle denotes the orientation of the principal material axis, x_1, within each ply. If a ply were repeated, a subscript would be used to denote the number of repeating plies. Thus, [0°/90°3/0°] indicates that the 90° ply is repeated three times.

Any laminate in which the ply stacking sequence below the midplane is a mirror image of the stacking sequence above the midplane is referred to as a symmetric laminate. For a symmetric laminate, such as a $[0°/90°_2/0°]$ plate, the notation can be abbreviated by using $[0°/90°]_S$, where the subscript S denotes that the stacking sequence is repeated symmetrically. Angle-ply laminates are denoted by $[0°/+45°/-45°]_S$, which can be abbreviated as $[0°/\pm45°]_S$. For laminates with repeating sets of plies—e.g., $[0°/\pm45°/0°/\pm45°]_S$, the abbreviated notation is of the form $[0°/\pm45°]_{2S}$. If a symmetric laminate contains a ply that is split at the centerline, a bar is used to denote the split. Thus, the laminate $[0°/90°/0°]$ can be abbreviated as $[0°/\overline{90°}]_S$. For unsymmetric laminates, a subscript T is often used to denote total laminate. For example, the laminate $[0°/90°]$ can be written as $[0°/90°]_T$. This assures the reader that the laminate is indeed unsymmetric and that a subscript S was not inadvertently omitted.

Balanced Laminates

Laminates in which each ply oriented at an angle of $+\theta$ ($\theta \neq 0°$ or $90°$) also contains a ply at $-\theta$ are referred to as balanced. Such composites are orthotropic relative to the x-y coordinate of the laminate. Thus, Eq 1a, b, and c with the subscripts 1 and 2 replaced by x and y, respectively, are applicable to balanced laminates.

Tensile Testing of Unidirectional Composites

Tensile tests on unidirectional composites (continuous and short fiber) are performed for the purpose of determining uniaxial tensile strength, Young's modulus, and Poisson's ratio. These test methods allow for the determination of the following properties of the lamina:

E_1 — Young's modulus in the fiber direction
E_2 — Young's modulus transverse to the fiber direction
v_{12} — Major Poisson's ratio
S_1 — Ultimate tensile strength in the fiber direction
S_2 — Ultimate tensile strength transverse to the fiber direction
e_1 — Ultimate tensile strain in the fiber direction
e_2 — Ultimate tensile strain transverse to the fiber direction

Actual specimen geometry depends on whether the composite has a polymeric or a metal matrix.

Tensile Testing

Polymeric-Matrix Specimen

Tensile testing of polymeric-matrix composites is based on ASTM Standard D 3039 (Ref 1). This method utilizes a straight-sided, constant-cross-section specimen with adhesively bonded end tabs for load introduction. The specimen is illustrated in Fig 2. For 0° unidirectional composites, the recommended specimen is 12.7 mm (0.5 in.) wide and 6 to 8 plies thick. In the case of 90° unidirectional composites, the recommended specimen is 25.4 mm (1.0 in.) wide and also 6 to 8 plies thick. Over-all specimen length is 229 mm (9 in.), with a test section of 152 mm (6 in.).

Specimens should be precision machined from plates with tabs bonded on. The ASTM standard recommends 0°/90° cross-ply tabs made from unidirectional nonwoven E-glass. Other orientations and/or tab materials may prove satisfactory. The major concern is that the tab material be strain-compatible with the composite being tested. Tab thickness should be 1.5 to 4 times the specimen thickness. As illustrated in Fig 2, the end tabs may be beveled with an angle ≥5° to the surface of the specimen. However, many workers have found that tabs without bevels work well. Redesign of the end tabs is in order if a significant fraction of the failures occur within one specimen width of the tabs. It should be noted that 90° specimens, because of their relatively low strength, often can be tested without end tabs. In this case, the specimen is wrapped with sandpaper to promote gripping friction.

Edges of the test specimen should be undamaged and parallel to within 0.127 mm (0.005 in.). Tab surfaces should be parallel to a reference surface within 0.0508 mm (0.002 in.).

Strain measurements can be obtained by utilizing an extensometer or electrical-resistance strain gages. If Poisson's ratio is to be determined, strain must be measured in both the longitudinal and transverse directions. Foil gages with a resistance of 350 Ω and a gage length of 3.175 mm (0.125 in.) or 6.35 mm (0.25 in.) have been found satisfactory for minimizing gage heating during testing. Strain gages are bonded to the specimen by use of an appropriate adhesive.

Wedge-section friction grips are utilized in conjunction with the tensile test. The specimen is aligned in the grips and monotonically loaded to failure at a recommended rate of 0.2 mm/min (0.0079 in./min). If there is any doubt concerning alignment, a specimen with three longitudinal strain gages, two across and the width of the front face and one on the center of the back face, can be monitored during loading and compared with the test specimen. These gages will allow bending in the thickness and width planes to be determined. A difference of more than 5% in strain readings in the linear portion of the stress-strain curve is an indication of excessive bending.

Many polymeric-matrix composites absorb moisture, which can cause reductions in mechanical properties. Thus, care must be exercised in maintaining such specimens in a dry environment prior to testing.

Metal-Matrix Specimen

Tensile testing of metal-matrix composites is based on ASTM Standard D 3552 (Ref 2). In addition to a straight-sided coupon similar to the ASTM D 3039 specimen for polymeric-matrix composites, two tapered specimen configurations, flat and round, are available in conjunction with this test method. Flat panels are produced by such techniques as diffusion bonding, whereas composites fabricated by various liquid infiltration and other methods used for producing massive materials are better suited to circular-cross-section shapes. The flat specimen configuration is shown in Fig 3. The circular-cross-section specimen is of limited use and will not be discussed here. A complete description of this specimen can be found in ASTM D 3552.

For 0° flat specimens, tabs are bonded to the grip section to cushion the end region from filament damage. Straight-sided coupons have a gage length of 50.8 mm (2 in.) or 76.2 mm (3 in.) and a width of 9.525 mm (0.375 in.) or 12.7 mm (0.5 in.), respectively. The recommended tab length, L_T, is

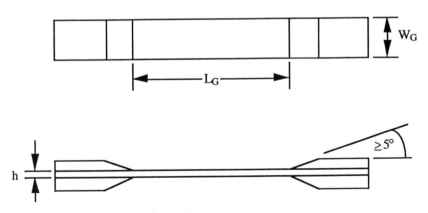

Fig 2. Polymeric-matrix tensile specimen

25.4 mm (1 in.). Tapered specimens have a gage length, L_G, of 25.4 mm (1 in.) and a gage-section width, W_G, of either 6.35 mm (0.25 in.) or 9.525 mm (0.375 in.). The shoulder and tab lengths, L_1 and L_T, respectively, should be 25.4 mm (1 in.). The radius of curvature of the shoulder, R, should be a minimum of 25.4 mm (1 in.). For tensile testing of materials in limited supply, a 25.4-mm (1-in.) gage section may be utilized in conjunction with a 6.35-mm (0.25-in.) gage width. The tab region may be reduced to 19.05 mm (0.75 in.) and the radius of the shoulder reduced to 12.7 mm (0.5 in.). It should be noted that with 0° tapered specimens, failure may tend to initiate at or near the fillet radius. If this occurs, a straight-sided specimen should be substituted.

Because 90° unidirectional composites tend to have low strength, larger widths are necessary to obtained reproducible data. In this case, a straight-sided coupon with a gage length of 25.4 mm (1 in.) and a width of 12.7 mm (0.5 in.) is recommended. The tab length remains at 25.4 mm (1 in.). If availability of material dictates a smaller specimen, the gage section may be reduced to 12.7 mm (0.5 in.).

As in the case of polymeric-matrix specimens, strain measurements can be obtained by utilizing an extensometer or strain gages. If Poisson's ratio is to be determined, strain must be measured in both the longitudinal and transverse directions. Gages should not measure less than 3 mm (0.1181 in.) in the longitudinal direction and not less than 1.5 mm (0.0591 in.) in the transverse direction. For specimens with short (12.7-mm, or 0.5-in.) gage sections, extensometers are not recommended.

Self-aligning wedge-type or lateral-pressure-type grips with serrated or knurled surfaces are required by ASTM Standard D 3552.

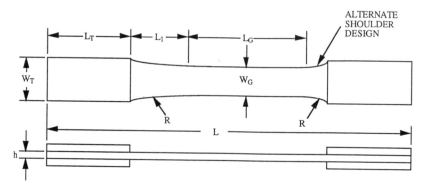

Fig 3. Metal-matrix tensile specimen

Gripping pressure should be sufficient to prevent specimen slippage without damaging the end tabs. Emery cloth or a similar material can be used to distribute the pressure more uniformly if the serrations are too coarse.

Mechanical properties of metal-matrix composites are very sensitive to specimen preparation. Special care should be taken in machining or trimming. For some types of metal-matrix composites, conventional machining methods are appropriate. In other cases, grinding or electrical discharge machining (EDM) should be used. Damaging vibrations must be minimized during machining, and in the EDM method the specimen must be mounted in such a manner as to ensure good electrical contact and thus prevent extraneous arcing and resulting specimen damage.

Data Reduction

Calculations of strength, Young's modulus, and Poisson's ratio are the same for both polymeric-matrix and metal-matrix composites. Tensile strength in the load direction is determined by dividing the maximum load by the cross-sectional area of the gage section:

$$S_L = \frac{P}{h \, W_G} \qquad \text{(Eq 4)}$$

where S_L is ultimate tensile strength in the load direction in megapascals or pounds per square inch; P is maximum load, in newtons or pounds (force); h is specimen thickness, in millimeters or inches; and W_G is the gage-section width of the specimen, in millimeters or inches.

Young's modulus in the load direction is determined from the slope of the load-strain curve in the linear region:

$$E_L = \frac{(\Delta P / \Delta \varepsilon)}{h \, W_G} \qquad \text{(Eq 5)}$$

where E_L is Young's modulus in the load direction, in megapascals or pounds per square inch; and $\Delta P / \Delta \varepsilon_L$ is the slope of the load-strain curve in the linear portion of the curve, where ε_L denotes the strain parallel to the load.

Tensile Testing

Poisson's ratio can be calculated from the relationship

$$\nu_{LT} = -\frac{\Delta\varepsilon_T}{\Delta\varepsilon_L} \qquad \text{(Eq 6)}$$

where ν_{LT} is Poisson's ratio relative to the load direction; and $\Delta\varepsilon_L/\Delta\varepsilon_T$ is the slope of the strain-strain curve, where ε_T denotes the strain transverse to the load direction.

Flexural Testing of Polymeric-Matrix Composites

An alternative approach to tensile testing of unidirectional polymeric-matrix composites involves the bending of beam-type specimens. The loading configurations involve three-point bending and four-point bending, as shown in Fig 4. It should be noted that the four-point flexural test is sometimes utilized with the load points at $L/3$ as well as at quarter points as shown. The quarter-point loading has been utilized primarily for high-modulus materials such as graphite/epoxy. These test methods are used for determining flexural strength and modulus. However, for unidirectional composites there is an assumption that flexural strength and modulus are equivalent to tensile strength and modulus. This assumption is valid only if the stress-strain curves in both tension and compression are linear with identical slopes and that failure is initiated on the tensile (bottom) side of the beam.

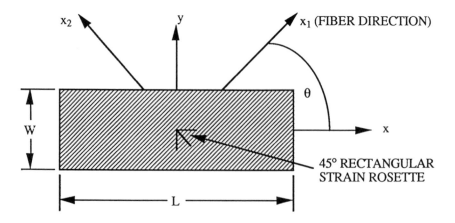

Fig 4. Off-axis tensile specimen

A testing machine having a controllable crosshead speed is used in conjunction with a loading fixture. Specific requirements for the fixture, including radius of the load noses and supports, can be found in ASTM Standard D 790 (Ref 3). Span-to-depth ratios, L/h, depend on the ratio of tensile strength parallel to the axis to interlaminar shear strength. For strength ratios less than 8:1, an L/h ratio of 16 is recommended. This is typical of fiberglass composites. For high-modulus materials such as graphite/epoxy, a value of $L/h = 32$ is recommended for 0° unidirectional composites. For 90° unidirectional properties of these materials, $L/h = 16$ is acceptable. Recommended specimen dimensions are also available in ASTM Standard D 790. Crosshead travel rate should be chosen such that the strain rate of the outer surface is approximately 0.01 mm/mm · min (0.01 in./in. · min). For both three-point and four-point flexure at quarter points,

$$\frac{dR}{dt} = \frac{(d\varepsilon/dt)L^2}{6h} \qquad \text{(Eq 7)}$$

where dR/dt is crosshead travel rate, in millimeters per minute or inches per minute; $d\varepsilon/dt$ is strain rate of outer surface, in millimeters per millimeter per minute or inches per inch per minute; L is span length, in millimeters or inches; and h is specimen thickness, in millimeters or inches.

The maximum tensile strength is determined from the relationships

$$S_b = \frac{3PL}{2bh^2} \text{ (three-point bending)} \qquad \text{(Eq 8a)}$$

and

$$S_b = \frac{3PL}{4bh^4} \text{ (four-point bending at quarter points)} \qquad \text{(Eq 8b)}$$

where S_b is ultimate tensile strength under bending load, in megapascals or pounds per square inch; P is maximum load, in newtons or pounds (force); and b is beam width, in millimeters or inches.

It should be noted that Eq 8a and 8b are valid only for materials for which the load-deflection curve is linear to failure. If any nonlinearity occurs, these relationships must be modified. Such modifications can be found can be found in ASTM Standard D 790.

Tensile Testing

For modulus determination, a deflectometer or an extensometer can be used to measure center deflection. If a deflectometer is used, the test must be stopped at a point where the stress-strain behavior is still linear and a reading taken. Owing to machine compliance, crosshead travel does not provide an accurate measure of deflection. Modulus is calculated from the relationships

$$E_b = \frac{(\Delta P/\Delta w_c)L^3}{4bh^3} \text{ (three-point bending)} \qquad \text{(Eq 9a)}$$

$$E_b = \frac{11(\Delta P/\Delta w_c)L^3}{64bh^3} \text{ (four-point bending at quarter points)} \qquad \text{(Eq 9b)}$$

where E_b is bending modulus (x-direction), in megapascals or pounds per square inch; w_c is deflection at the center of the beam, in millimeters or inches; and $\Delta P/\Delta w_c$ is the slope of the load-deflection curve in the linear region.

For unidirectional composites in which the in-plane modulus is very high compared with the interlaminar shear modulus, Eq 9 must be corrected for shear deformation, as outlined in ASTM Standard D 790. The effect of shear deformation is a function of the span-to-depth ratio, L/h. Thus, an alternative method involves measuring bending modulus for increasing values of L/h until a constant value is obtained.

The center section of the four-point specimen is under uniform bending, which leads to a constant stress at the outer surface of the beam. For this reason, four-point bending is often preferred to three-point bending.

Failure modes present a major difficulty with flex tests for determining tensile properties. In particular, failure is often initiated on the compression side of the beam, making the test invalid for determination of tensile strength. Although the test method is not recommended for generating design data, it is often used as a simple test for quality control.

Tensile Testing of Off-Axis Unidirectional Composites

It is often desirable to measure unidirectional properties at some angle relative to the principal material coordinate system (x_1-x_2 axes).

This is accomplished by utilizing an off-axis tensile specimen consisting of a laminate with all layers having a fiber orientation, θ, with respect to the longitudinal axis (x-axis), as shown in Fig 1. This test method is used to measure off-axis modulus and strength. It also provides a method of applying multiaxial stresses relative to the principal material coordinate system.

The presence of shear coupling causes additional consideration in the case of off-axis tensile testing. For the case of uniaxial tension in the x-direction, the stress-strain relationships (Eq 2a-c) reduce to

$$\varepsilon_x = \frac{1}{E_x}\,\sigma_x,\ \varepsilon_y = -\frac{\nu_{xy}}{E_x}\,\sigma_x,\ \gamma_{xy} = \frac{\eta_x}{E_x}\,\sigma_x \qquad \text{(Eq 10)}$$

Thus, shear coupling is present—that is, shear strain will be induced by the uniaxial tensile stress. The presence of the shear coupling phenomenon causes additional consideration in the off-axis test compared with the method for orthotropic composites covered by ASTM Standard D 3039. In particular, clamping of the tensile coupon at the ends prohibits local rotation (due to shear) of the specimen, which induces a nonuniform strain field in the gage section. It has been shown by Pagano and Halpin (Ref 4), however, that a uniform state of stress and strain will exist at the center of an off-axis tensile coupon if the length-to-width ratio, L/W, is sufficiently large. The exact dimensions necessary to accomplish this depend on the degree of shear coupling as measured by the value of the shear coupling coefficient, η_x. If an apparent modulus, $E_x{}^*$, is experimentally determined in the usual manner for an off-axis tensile coupon, the error introduced by shear coupling can be estimated from the expression (Ref 4)

$$E_x = (1 - \eta)\,E_x{}^* \qquad \text{(Eq 11)}$$

where

$$\eta = \frac{3\eta_x}{\left(\dfrac{3E_x}{G_{xy}} + \dfrac{2L^2}{W^2}\right)}$$

and where E_x is the actual Young's modulus in the x-direction (load direction) in megapascals or pounds per square inch; $E_x{}^*$ is the apparent

Tensile Testing

Young's modulus in the x-direction (load direction) as determined from the slope of the stress-strain curve in the usual manner, in megapascals or pounds per square inch; G_{xy} is the shear modulus relative to the x-y plane, in megapascals or pounds per square inch; L is the specimen length between tabs, in millimeters or inches; and W in the width of a straight-sided tensile coupon, in millimeters or inches. Thus, η is a direct measure of the error involved in the observed modulus. A cursory examination of Eq 11 reveals that η vanishes for decreasing values of η_x or increasing ratios of E_x/G_{xy} and L/W. Because elastic properties are fixed for a particular material and off-axis angle, the experimentalist can reduce η only by increasing L/W.

The test specimen and procedure are the same as described in ASTM Standard D 3039. If the off-axis specimen is used as a means of introducing multiaxial stress relative to the principal material coordinate system, a three-element (rosette) gage (see Fig 4) is necessary to determine the stress-strain response parallel to the fibers, transverse to the fibers, and in longitudinal shear. The data-reduction procedure consists of recording the load and the outputs of the three strain gages. Stresses relative to the material coordinate system can be calculated from the relationship

$$\sigma_1 = m^2 \sigma_x, \sigma_2 = m^2 \sigma_x, \tau_{12} = -mn \, \sigma_x \qquad \text{(Eq 12)}$$

where $m = \cos \theta$ and $n = \sin \theta$. The axial stress, σ_x, is determined by dividing the load by the cross-sectional area. Strains relative to the material coordinate system can be determined from the strain-rosette in the following manner:

$$\varepsilon_1 = m \, (m - n) \, \varepsilon_x + n \, (n - m) \, \varepsilon_y + 2mn \, \varepsilon_{45°} \qquad \text{(Eq 13a)}$$

$$\varepsilon_2 = m \, (m + n) \, \varepsilon_x + n \, (n + m) \, \varepsilon_y - 2mn \, \varepsilon_{45°} \qquad \text{(Eq 13b)}$$

$$\gamma_{12} = (m^2 + 2mn - n^2) \, \varepsilon_x + (m^2 - 2mn - n^2) \, \varepsilon_y + 2 \, (m^2 - n^2) \, \varepsilon_{45°} \qquad \text{(Eq 13c)}$$

where ε_x, ε_y, and $\varepsilon_{45°}$ are the strains in the x, y, and 45° directions, respectively, as measured by the rosette. If one of the three elastic constants E_1, E_2, and v_{12} are known, then the remaining two constants can be determined from Eq 12 and 13 in conjunction with Eq 1. It should be noted that the shear modulus, G_{12}, can also be determined from this test.

In addition to the end constraint problem due to shear coupling, this test method is sensitive to the accuracy of the desired fiber orientation.

A 1° or 2° error in the fiber orientation can cause large errors in the data developed from Eq 12 and 13.

Tensile Testing of Orthotropic Laminates

Tensile testing of symmetric, balanced laminates (continuous filament) and multidirectional composites (short fiber) are performed for the purpose of determining uniaxial tensile strength, Young's modulus, and Poisson's ratio. These test methods allow for the determination of the following properties of the laminate and/or multidirectional composite:

E_x — Effective Young's modulus of the laminate in the loading direction

ν_{xy} — Effective Poisson's ratio of the laminate

S_x — Uniaxial ultimate tensile strength of the laminate in the loading direction

e_x — Uniaxial ultimate tensile strain of the laminate in the loading direction.

Test Specimen

The test specimen and procedures are essentially the same as those previously discussed for unidirectional composites. Thus, polymeric-matrix composites are covered by ASTM Standard D 3039 and metal-matrix composites by ASTM D 3552. The requirement that the laminate be balanced and symmetric ensures that the effective in-plane properties are orthotropic with respect to the loading direction (x-y axes), and the stress-strain response is given by Eq 1 with the subscripts 1 and 2 replaced by x and y, respectively.

For polymeric-matrix laminates, the test-specimen geometry should be the same as that given for 90° unidirectional composites. In the case of metal-matrix laminates, the specimen design for strengths expected to exceed 689 MPa (100 ksi) should be the same as for 0° unidirectional composites. For laminates with the strengths lower than 689 MPa (100 ksi), the design should be identical to that for 90° unidirectional specimens.

Tensile Testing

Data Reduction

Composite properties can be calculated from Eq 4 to 6. As in the case of unidirectional composites, two-element strain-gage data is required if Poisson's ratio is to be measured.

Flexural Testing

For multidirectional laminates, the strength and modulus, as determined from a bending test, will depend on laminate stacking sequence, requiring the data to be interpreted in conjunction with laminated beam theory (Ref 3). In addition, bending modulus and strength do not necessarily correlate with tensile modulus and strength, even when failure initiates on the tensile side of the beam. Thus, flexural tests are not recommended for multidirectional laminates as a method for obtaining tensile properties.

Free-Edge Effects

The presence of a boundary layer in the vicinity of the free edge of a laminate in which the state of stress is three-dimensional in nature has been well established (Ref 5-8). In testing of laminates, it is important to recognize the presence of this boundary layer and its effect on the surface strain distribution in that region, and the potential deleterious effects of the associated interlaminar stresses on the laminate strength.

In classical lamination theory, the ply stresses for symmetric laminates under in-plane loading (such as in a tensile test) are assumed to be planar. This assumption is accurate for interior regions removed from discontinuities such as free edges. However, as mentioned in the previous paragraph, there is a boundary-layer region near the laminate free edge where the state of stress is three-dimensional in nature. The boundary layer is the region in which the stress transfer between plies is accomplished through interlaminar stresses. Boundary-layer width depends on the elastic properties of the plies, the ply orientations, and the laminate stacking geometry. A rule of thumb (Ref 6) for polymer-matrix composites containing brittle resins is that the boundary-layer region is equal to approximately one laminate thickness. Thus, tensile specimens in which the width-to-thickness is not large will be dominated by the edge region.

The major concern in the case of tensile testing of laminates is the potential for delamination-induced failures, which initiate in the boundary region and may influence laminate tensile strength. In addition, the presence of the boundary layer prevents the experimentalist from determining subsurface response from surface strain measurements.

Interlaminar stress transfer in the boundary region can be broken into two fundamental mechanisms. The first mechanism, referred to as Mode I (Ref 9), occurs in laminates of the class [±θ]s, in which the mismatch between shear coupling coefficients between the +θ and −θ layers induces interlaminar shear stresses under uniaxial tension. In the second mechanism, referred to as Mode II (Ref 9), interlaminar normal stresses are generated as the result of a mismatch in Poisson's ratios of the plies. This mechanism occurs, for example, in laminates of the class [0°/90°]s. For Mode II mechanism laminates, the interlaminar normal stress at the free edge may be either tensile or compressive. In the case of [0°/190°]s laminates subjected to uniaxial tension (x-direction), the normal stress at the free edge will be tensile (peel stress). If the stacking sequence is reversed—that is, for [90°/0°]s laminates—the interlaminar normal stress at the free edge will be compressive. For complex laminate geometries—for example, [0°/ ± θ]s laminates—both interlaminar shear and normal stresses will be present in the boundary region when the laminate is subjected to uniaxial tension.

The nature of the interlaminar stresses in the boundary region can be characterized by using classical lamination theory in conjunction with a free-body diagram (Ref 7).

Application of Tensile Tests to Design

It is often desired to use coupon-level data for design purposes. Thus, it is appropriate to consider the merits, for design purposes, of tensile-test data generated in accordance with ASTM Standard D 3039 for polymeric-matrix composites and Standard D 3552 for metal-matrix composites. Because both of these test methods involve straight-sided specimens, one must be careful that failures do not consistently occur near the end tabs. Even for the tapered metal-matrix specimens, consistent failure near the fillets are of concern.

In addition to these obvious pitfalls, one has to be concerned with the over-all failure processes that occur in laminates. In particular cases for which the initial failure mode is delamination due to free edges, one must carefully assess whether such a failure process represents how the material will behave in the structure or whether the data is an artifact of the test method. In fact, failure modes produced at the coupon level should always be evaluated as to their applicability to behavior in a structure. This is particularly true for multidirectional fiber-reinforced composites.

Other considerations include the influence of "first ply failure" on design. In particular, matrix cracking (first ply failure) may occur far below ultimate failure in a multidirectional laminate. The effect of first ply failure on the usefulness of the laminate in the structure is an important design consideration that is not of concern to the experimentalist performing tensile tests. It may be important, however, for the experimentalist to determine first ply failure. This is usually done by observing a plateau in the stress-strain curve. For fiber-dominated laminates, such as [0°/90°]s, observance of a plateau may require monitoring of the transverse stress-strain curve, because matrix failure in the 90° plies will not have an influence on the longitudinal stress-strain curve.

References

1. ASTM Standard D 3039, "Standard Test Method for Tensile Properties of Fiber-Resin Composites," *ASTM Standards and Literature References for Composite Materials,* 2nd ed., ASTM, 1990, p 26-30
2. ASTM Standard D 3552, "Standard Test Method for Tensile Properties of Fiber-Reinforced Metal Matrix Composites," *ASTM Standards and Literature References for Composite Materials,* 2nd ed., ASTM, 1990, p 70-74
3. ASTM Standard D 790, "Standard Test Method for Unreinforced and Reinforced Plastics and Electrical Insulating Materials," *ASTM Standards and Literature References for Composite Materials,* 2nd ed., ASTM, 1990, p 296-305
4. N.J. Pagano and J.C. Halpin, Influence of End Constraint in the Testing of Anisotropic Bodies, *J. Compos. Mater.,* Vol 2 (No. 1), Jan 1968, p 18-31
5. A.H. Puppo and H.A. Evensen, Interlaminar Shear in Laminated Composites Under Generalized Plane Stress, *J. Compos. Mater.,* Vol 4 (No. 2), Aug 1970, p 204-221
6. R.B. Pipes and N.J. Pagano, Interlaminar Stresses in Composite Laminates Under Uniform Axial Extension, *J. Compos. Mater.,* Vol 4 (No. 4), Oct 1970, p 538-548
7. N.J. Pagano and R.B. Pipes, Influence of Stacking Sequence on Laminate Strength, *J. Compos. Mater.,* Vol 5 (No. 1), Jan 1971, p 50-57
8. N.J. Pagano and R.B. Pipes, Some Observations on the Interlaminar Strength of Composite Laminates, *Int. J. Mech. Sci.,* Vol 15, 1973, p 679-688
9. J.M. Whitney, I.M. Daniel, and R.B. Pipes, *Experimental Mechanics of Fiber Reinforced Composite Materials,* Monograph No. 4, 2nd ed., Society for Experimental Mechanics, 1984

Index

Adhesives
  standards for tensile testing of, 59
  for strain gages, 40–41
Aluminum
  yield strength, 72
  Young's modulus, 63, 72
Aluminum alloys, dynamic strain aging or serrated yielding in, 97
Anelasticity, in metals and alloys, 64–71
Anisotropy. *See also* Normal anisotropy; Planar anisotropy
  in elastomers, 137
  in plastics, 106, 111–114
  of sheet metal specimens, 19–21
Annealing, effect on hardness of coldrolled brass, 85
ASTM standards, for tensile testing, 59, 140–142, 188, 189, 190, 192–196, 198, 199
Atmosphere control, in high-temperature tensile testing of ceramics, 174–175
Axial alignment, of tensile specimens, 22–24, 50, 51

Backings, for strain gages, 40–41
Backlash, and screw-driven testing machines, 28
Ball-on-ring test, for ceramics, 162, 166, 175
Bending tests. *See* Flexure tests
Brass
  cartridge, effect of cold rolling on grain shape, 83
  effect of annealing on hardness, 85

Brass (Continued)
  effect of cold work on hardness and strength, 76
  effect of cold work on strength and ductility, 82
  and solid-solution strengthening, 75
Brazilian test. See Diametral compression test
Bridgman correction for true stress, 13–15
British standards, for tensile testing of various materials, 59
Brittle materials, stress-strain curve, 86
Bronze, and solid-solution strengthening, 75
Bronze Age, 75
Buttonhead grips, 46, 155, 157–158

Calibration, of load-measurement systems, 33
Ceramic-matrix composites, tensile testing of, 147–181
Ceramics
  advantages of, 148
  for environmental chamber testing, 46
  limitations of, 148–149
  tensile testing of, 147–181
  Cold grip test, for ceramics, 171,172
Cold rolling, effect on grain shape in cartridge brass, 83
Cold work
  effect on flow stress of titanium, 81

Laminate theory, 198
Laser systems, for strain measurement in ceramics, 173–174
Linear variable differential transformers, 34–36, 171
"Little Giant" tensile-testing machine, 25
Load cells, for strain gages, 31–33
Load transfer, in direct tensile testing, 154–158
Lubrication, and gripping, 56–57
Lüders bands, 78–79
LVDT. *See* Linear variable differential transformers

Materials evaluation, using tensile test data, 128–130
Materials selection, using tensile test data, 130–131
Maxwell element, 108
Mechanical grips, 154, 155
Metal-matrix composites, tensile testing of, 189–191
Metals, standards for tensile testing of, 59
Metals and alloys, tensile testing of, 61–104
Modulus, of elastomers, 136
Monel, and solid-solution strengthening, 75

Necking, 9, 10–14, 93
  effect on tensile testing of plastics, 112
  in plastics, 114–116
Newtonian dashpots, and viscoelasticity, 107
Nickel
  stress-strain curve, 80
  yield strength, 72
  Young's modulus, 72
Nonaxiality. *See* Axial alignment
Normal anisotropy, 21
Notched specimens, 113

Oak Ridge National Laboratory, 157
Off-axis tensile testing, 194–197
Offset yield strength, defined, 7, 8–9, 77
Olsen, Tinius, 25–26
Optical encoders, for screw-driven testing machines, 28–29
Optical metallography, to characterize grain structure defects, 73
Orthotropic laminates
  free-edge effects, 198–199

Orthotropic laminates (Continued)
  tensile testing of, 197–199

Peel stress, 199
Percent elongation, 11. See also Elongation
  defined, 10
  Percent reduction in area, 11
  defined, 10
Phase boundaries, and yield strength, 76–77
Pinned grips, 155, 157
Planar anisotropy, 21
Plastic deformation, 5–6, 8
  of ceramics, 148
  defined, 5
  of metals and alloys, 63, 72, 78, 85
  and stress-strain curves, 88
  of a wire, 6
Plasticity, 114–116
  effect on tensile testing, 112
  and yielding, 72–77
Plastics
  sensitivity to processing conditions, 127–128
  standards for tensile testing of, 59
  tensile testing of, 105–133
  testing requirements for, 117–128
Pneumatic grips, 43–44, 154, 155, 156
Poisson's ratio
  defined, 5
  for fiber-reinforced composites, 188,189–192
  for metals and alloys, 66
  for orthotropic laminates, 195
Polymeric-matrix composites
  flexural testing of, 192–194
  tensile testing of, 188–189
Polymers, 135, 137
  linear, inhomogeneous yielding of, 8
Portevin-LeChatelier effect, 98
Proportional limit
  defined, 8, 71
  effect of accuracy of measurement on, 71
  for metals and alloys, 71–72

Reduction in area. *See* Percent reduction in area
Refractory metals, for environmental chamber testing, 46
Ring-on-ring test, for ceramics, 162, 166, 175

204

Titanium (Continued)
  Young's modulus, 72
Total strain, defined, 8
Toughness
  of ceramic-matrix composites, 162
  of metals and alloys, 87, 89–91
Transducers, 27
  for plastics, 121
  pressure-displacement, 33
Transformers, linear variable differential, 34–36, 171
Transmission electron microscopy, to characterize line defects, 73, 74
True strain, defined, 11–12
True stress
  Bridgman correction for, 13–15
  defined, 11–12
True stress-strain, in metals and alloys, 93–95
Trussed beam test, for ceramics, 160, 161

Ultimate elongation, of elastomers, 136
Ultimate strength. *See also* Tensile strength
  of metals and alloys, 86–87
Unidirectional composites, off-axis, 193–197

Viscoelasticity
  linear, 107
  nonlinear, 109
  in plastics, 106–110
Viscosity, Newtonian, 107
Voigt element, 108
Vulcanization, 138–140

Wedge-type grips, 42, 43, 154–156

Weibull strength distributions, 151
Wheatstone bridge, 41
Work hardening
  effect on tensile testing of plastics, 112
Work hardening
  in plastics, 114–116

Yielding
  effect on grain size on, 79–80
  and post-yield tensile behavior, 115
Yield points, 9
  in metals and alloys, 78–79, 98
  in plastics, 126
Yield strength
  and alloy content, 75
  copper alloys, 75
  defined, 8–9, 72, 77
  metals and alloys, 62–63, 72–77
  offset, defined, 7, 8–9, 77
  and toughness, 91
Yield stress, in plastics, 116
Young's modulus, 12
  aluminum, 63, 72
  copper, 63
  defined, 5
  fiber-reinforced composites, 189
  iron, 63
  loading-rate effects on, 68
  metals and alloys, 64, 68, 72
  nickel, 72
  orthotropic laminates, 195
  silver, 72
  steel (mild), 72
  titanium, 72
  and toughness, 91